SPORE LIBERATION

SPORE
LIBERATION

By

C. T. INGOLD

CLARENDON PRESS
OXFORD
1965

Oxford University Press, Amen House, London E.C.4

GLASGOW NEW YORK TORONTO MELBOURNE WELLINGTON
BOMBAY CALCUTTA MADRAS KARACHI LAHORE DACCA
CAPE TOWN SALISBURY NAIROBI IBADAN ACCRA
KUALA LUMPUR HONG KONG

Printed in Northern Ireland at The Universities Press, Belfast

This book is dedicated to
Nora Ingold.

CONTENTS

PREFACE

THIS little book deals with those aspects of spore liberation which have interested me during the past few years. In no sense is it a revision of my 'Dispersal in Fungi' first published in 1953. Indeed, any overlap between the two works is very slight. Although the present book is devoted in the main to the Fungi, a final chapter on 'Spore liberation in bryophytes' has been included, first because this interests me and secondly because it embraces much of the non-mycological material of 'Spore Discharge in Land Plants' published in 1939 and long out of print. I have repeatedly been pressed to make this treatment of bryophytes again available.

Authorities for specific names have been deliberately omitted. Their inclusion would have made the book less readable and I believe that, in a book of this kind, little or no ambiguity is involved in this procedure.

I have prepared the majority of the text-figures myself, although a number of these have already appeared in papers and in my earlier books. However, a number are derived from other sources. In this connexion my sincere thanks are due to the Hafner Publishing Co. of New York for permission to reproduce a number of figures from their excellent reprint of Buller's Researches on Fungi; to Dr. P. H. Gregory and Leonard Hill Ltd. of London for allowing me to use two figures from 'The Microbiology of the Atmosphere'; to Dr. H. Brodie for letting me reproduce his well-known and beautiful figure of *Cyathus*, to Dr. R. K. Benjamin for the use of his fine illustration of *Spirodactylon* and to Dr. A. Fonda for kindly permitting me to quote from his unpublished researches on the theory of fall of ellipsoidal particles.

I am particularly grateful for the assistance given by my colleagues in the Department of Botany of Birkbeck College, especially Dr. B. E. Plunkett who read my book in typescript and made a number of valuable suggestions for its improvement, and Brenda Marshall for her help particularly in connexion with my studies of *Sordaria*.

Birkbeck College   C.T.I.
Jan. 1965.

I

FORM AND FUNCTION
OF FUNGAL SPORES

Dispersal seems to be a problem for all kinds of organism. Each species of plant or animal occurs in a circumscribed geographical area; it has a fairly definite range. This may be of small extent. Indeed a species may be limited to one little oceanic island or to a single mountain top. On the other hand it may range over almost the whole of the habitable world. Even where the range is now great, the species almost certainly started in one spot. It has been argued that the widely-ranging species tend to be the older, whilst comparable species that at present occupy small areas tend to be young beginners. Extension of geographical range is a feature of the history of each species and for this extension some mechanism of dispersal is a necessity.

Most animals exploit their immediate territory and extend their range by their own movements, but the fixed organism whether an animal such as a sponge or coral, or a plant must rely on detachable units for dispersal. Sponges and corals have their free-swimming larval stages, flowering plants their seeds, and fungi, ferns, mosses, liverworts, and seaweeds their microscopic spores.

The necessity for dispersal is not confined to the extension of geographical area. Individuals within the general range of each species are usually limited to certain ecological niches and if these are scattered the dispersal mechanism must be adequate to provide propagules in the right places when and where opportunities offer.

Again dispersal has a genetic importance. Each species at any time is more or less in equilibrium with its environment both physical and biotic. But this environment may change over the years and a species, if it is to survive, must be capable of adjusting itself to these altering conditions. Here the degree

I

of genetic variability available for selection may be of great importance. Dispersal may be of significance in giving the opportunity for new variability, when it arises in a species at a certain point in its range, to spread amongst the whole population. This spread of new variability may be achieved by the dispersal of reproductive units, such as seeds and spores, capable of giving rise to new individuals, but it may also be achieved by the spread of pollen grains in higher plants. A similar example from the fungi is the dispersal of pycnidiospores of rusts which can, like pollen grains, transport genes, but cannot grow directly into new individuals.

It should be noted, however, that although efficient dispersal may spread new genes amongst a population and so increase the evolutionary plasticity of a species, it tends to operate against actual speciation, since effective dispersal breaks down isolation on which species differentiation so largely depends.

To sum up it may be said that dispersal is of significance for the maintenance of the population within its existing range, for the extension of the range of a species, and for its genetical development.

Fungi reproduce and spread mainly by spores. These, as in other cryptogams, are microscopic units mostly unicellular although not infrequently multicellular and contain some food reserve, usually oil or glycogen. Many fungal spores are meiospores, as in bryophytes and pteridophytes, with a meiosis involved in their formation. Ascospores, basidiospores, and the spores in the sporangia of Mycetozoa are of this nature. However, spore production may be quite unrelated to meiosis. This is true, for example, of the great range of conidial forms classified in Fungi Imperfecti, of the conidial stages of Ascomycetes, of the uredospores of Uredinales (rusts), and of the sporangiospores of Mucorales.

Nearly all spores are essentially dispersive units. Some, however, are merely resting structures that can tide the fungus over an unfavourable period such as the intense cold of winter or prolonged drought. To this category belong most rust teleutospores, although some are also dispersive, and the oospores of

Phycomycetes. Again zygospores of Mucorales are resting rather than dispersal spores, but the part they play in the general biology of these fungi is far from clear.

The great majority of spores have firm cell walls, but the zoospore of water-moulds is naked, although having come to rest it then secretes a wall prior to germination.

Although essentially microscopic, spores of fungi vary greatly in size and shape. Most are, however, spherical or ovoid with a diameter in the range 5–50 μ, but the ascospores of some lichens are nearly visible with the unaided eye. For example the two-celled ascospore of *Varicellaria microsticta* may be as large as $350 \times 115 \mu$, nearly as big as the smallest orchid seeds. Many spores are long and thread-like. Thus the septate ascospores of *Cordyceps militaris* may be 500 μ long but only 2 μ wide. In some fungi the spore is a branched structure, a feature particularly characteristic of aquatic Hyphomycetes.

Although single spores are microscopic, in the mass they may become conspicuous as in the spore print of a toadstool or in the smoke-like cloud rising from a puffing *Peziza*, or from a ripe puff-ball (*Lycoperdon* sp.) bombarded by falling rain drops.

Spores vary in colour. Many are transparent and colourless appearing white in the mass; but they may be yellow, pink, purple, brown, or black, and indeed spore colour is an important taxonomic character particularly in the Agaricales. The colour of spores is due largely to pigmentation in the spore wall, although yellow-orange carotinoid pigments dissolved in oil drops in the cytoplasm may also contribute, particularly in the uredospores of rusts.

Apart from pigmentation, the wall of the spore may vary considerably. It can be thin or thick and either smooth or variously ornamented.

In this chapter we are concerned with the question: are the considerable variations in fungal spores entirely haphazard, or can some at least be related to function? The morphologist of higher plants reviewing the range of dispersal units, be they seeds or indehiscent fruits, cannot fail to be impressed by the relationship of structure to dispersal. It would indeed be strange if natural selection, which seems to have operated so

3

effectively in shaping the propagules of flowering plants, should not have had some influence on fungal spores.

Natural selection could operate on form in connexion with any of the critical episodes of a spore's existence: liberation, transport, arrest on a suitable substratum, or germination. Further any of the features of a spore—size, shape, colour, or contents—might have adaptive significance.

We may in the first place consider spore size. For a spore that is violently discharged, the distance to which it is thrown is greatly affected by its size. For a microscopic spherical projectile the distance of horizontal throw (D) is given by (Buller, 1909):

$$D = H\left(\frac{2(\sigma-\rho)r^2}{9\,\mu}\right)$$

where H = initial velocity of discharge,
   σ = density of projectile,
   ρ = density of air,
   μ = viscosity of air,
   r = radius of the spherical projectile.

With most fungal spores the density is approximately 1·0 and that of the air so small that it can be neglected. The viscosity of the air is practically constant. Thus for a given initial velocity of discharge (the 'muzzle velocity' of the spore gun) the distance of discharge is given by:

$$D = Kr^2$$

where K is a constant. Hence the distance of discharge, with a particular initial velocity of launching, is proportional to the square of the radius of the projectile. Further, with particles of the size of most fungal spores, there is no significant difference between the distance of horizontal and of vertical throw.

The biological significance of violent discharge seems to be that the spores are thereby set free from the parent body in such a manner that they stand a reasonable chance of adequate dispersal. In Ascomycetes where the asci shoot spores to 0·2–60 cm, according to the species, discharge is often sufficiently violent to carry spores through the boundary layer of still air into the turbulent layers above. It may well be that large spores, tending to be shot to a greater distance, stand a better chance than smaller ones of effective dispersal on this account. However, as we shall see later, this advantage may be counter-balanced by a tendency for earlier fall-out.

It is amongst the specialized coprophilous Ascomycetes that large spore size seems to be of special significance and appears to be most clearly adaptive.

In the coprophilous fungi which grows so regularly and abundantly on the dung of herbivores, the spores eaten with the grass travel uninjured through the animal and may even be stimulated to germinate during this passage. In the deposited dung the mycelium develops, and in due course fruiting occurs. The next step for the fungus is to get its spores onto the grass around the dung. Some species achieve this by a capacity to shoot their spores to relatively great distances, combined with an ability, by means of positive phototropism, to train their spore guns on the general target area. Many coprophilous fungi are Ascomycetes. Most Ascomycetes discharge their spores to a distance of 0·5–5 cm, but some coprophilous species have much greater ranges, not, however, by virtue of greater violence of discharge, but simply by having larger spores. In a number of species the advantage is still further enhanced by all spores of an ascus being glued together to form a single projectile.

Amongst Discomycetes *Dasyobolus immersus* is an outstanding example (Fig. 1). In the minute apothecium only a few asci ripen each day, but these are relatively enormous. The purple spores are 50–75 μ × 30–40 μ and each is surrounded by mucilage which glues the ascus complement of eight into a firm mass always discharged as a whole and to a distance of around 60 cm. Amongst coprophilous Pyrenomycetes a very similar example is *Podospora fimicola* (Fig. 1). The black, oval spore 60–70 μ × 25–30 μ has a basal colourless cellular appendage about 70 μ long and 5–10 μ wide. From the bottom of this colourless cell and from the apex of the spore long worm-like mucilaginous appendages are extruded. These rope the eight spores together so that generally they are discharged as a single

5

projectile to a distance of 30–40 cm. In Ascomycetes large spore size and a strong tendency for spores to stick together are striking features of many coprophilous species. Nevertheless, it must be conceded that the largest known ascospores belong to lignicolous lichens of the genera *Varicellaria* and *Pertusaria*, and in quite a number of non-coprophilous fungi, for example in

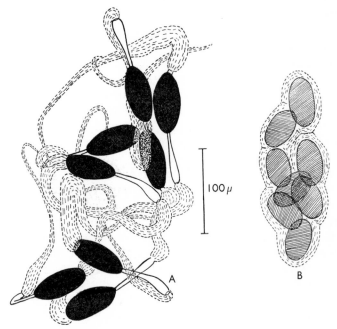

100 μ

FIG. 1. A, *Podospora fimicola* and B, *Dasyobolus immersus*. Spore mass discharged from ascus.

the lignicolous *Daldinia concentrica*, there is a tendency for the spores of an ascus to stick together on discharge.

Another way in which some coprophilous Ascomycetes achieve a greater distance of throw is by increasing the number of spores in the ascus rather than the size of individual spores. In *Podospora setosa*, for example, although the size of individual spores is comparatively small, the number approximates to 128 and this spore-mass is discharged to a distance of about

30 cm (Callaghan, 1962). Incidentally it should be noted that, although the spores may be discharged as a single mass, they no doubt become separated from one another during passage through the gut of the animal. But although the multispored ascus is a striking feature of some coprophilous Ascomycetes, being found not only in some species of *Podospora* but also in certain species of *Rhyparobius* and *Ascozonus*, asci with a large number of spores are quite well-known amongst lignicolous fungi (e.g. *Tympanis* spp.).

Having considered the possible adaptive significance of spore size in relation to take-off, the initial step in dispersal, we may now consider the selective pressures operating in connexion with the actual transport through the air. But first we must briefly take account of the general principles of aerial dispersal.

The modern view pictures dispersal from a point source steadily liberating spores as rather like the plume of smoke from a factory chimney. The spore cloud takes the form of a horizontal cone with its apex resting at the point of spore liberation (Fig. 2). As the cloud moves downwind in the turbulent air it is diluted by mixing with peripheral eddies. At any point its diameter is on the average proportional to the distance it has travelled and thus the conical form is achieved. The mean concentration of spores at any cross section of the cloud is inversely proportional to the distance from the source but concentrations are greater around the horizontal axis of the cone than nearer its surface. In nature a spore cloud is usually generated at or near ground level and, in consequence, its base drags along the surface losing spores steadily by various types of deposition as it proceeds. Gregory (1945) has developed formulae to describe dispersal in mathematical terms based on Sutton's theory of eddy diffusion. In these formulae no account is taken of spore size, since it is assumed that the rate of fall of spores in still air is of little account in relation to the movements which occur within the eddies of a body of air in turbulent motion. Actually this rate of fall varies from 2·0–2·78 cm/sec for the very large spores of *Helminthosporium sativum* down to 0·05 cm/sec for the minute ones of *Lycoperdon pyriforme*.

7

However, even the relatively rapid terminal velocity of *Helminthosporium* spores in still air is small when compared with that of a caryopsis of thistle (*Cirsium arvense*) which has a rate of fall of 16·8 cm/sec.

Schrödter (1960) criticizes the neglect of rate of spore fall as a factor in aerial dispersion. He says 'The velocity of fall is an

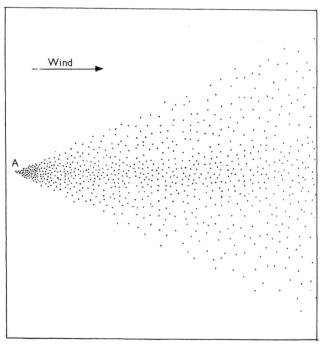

Fig. 2. Diagram of a spore-cloud diffusing downwind from a point source, A.

extremely important factor in determining the range of flight and cannot be neglected in the problem of dissemination'. It is quite clear that, in the dispersal of propagules liberated into the air by plants, size must become important at some level. The difference between the potential for aerial dispersal of an acorn and a pine seed is obvious. The question is whether there is any significance in differences in size at the level of microscopic particles. It is difficult to reach any firm conclusions in this matter on theoretical grounds, but it is impossible to deny the strength of Schrödter's argument that 'the gravitational fall is always going on. Even in turbulent air when the net movement is upward, gravitational fall continues'.

Evidence bearing on the matter comes from the work of Sreeramulu and Ramalingam (1961). In a series of five experiments of the Stepanov type (Stepanov, 1935) they liberated a mixture of $9 \cdot 39 \times 10^8$ *Lycopodium* spores ($32 \cdot 3 \ \mu$ diam.) and 9×10^9 *Podaxis* spores ($14 \times 11 \ \mu$) at a height of 50 cm. Spores were then trapped on vaselined horizontal microscope slides placed on the ground along a series of radii extending downwind for about 10 metres and 30–50° on either side of this direction. The wind speeds varied in the five experiments from $4 \cdot 3$ m/sec to $0 \cdot 8$ m/sec. In spite of the fact that about ten times as many *Podaxis* spores were liberated, the total catch on all the slides in these experiments was 12230 *Lycoperdon* spores and only 5480 of the much smaller ones of *Podaxis*. They concluded that 'the rate of deposition of the two types from suspension in the spore cloud was directly proportional to the individual spore volumes'. These results suggest that spore size is certainly an important factor in dispersal. It seems very likely, therefore, that natural selection has tended to limit the size of spores transported by air.

It is only in relatively recent years that aerobiologists have given their attention to the problems involved in the deposition of spores, and here again it is clear that spore size is highly significant. The principal mechanisms concerned are sedimentation under the influence of gravity, impaction, including turbulent deposition (which would deposit as many spores on the lower as on the upper surface of a horizontal slide exposed a foot or so above ground level), and rain wash-out.

It is important to consider the target, as it were, of a fungus. Since the great majority of spores are wasted by coming to rest in unsuitable places or under conditions unfavourable for their germination, selection might tend to favour any feature which predisposed spores to arrest on a suitable substratum. There is, for example, evidence that the relatively large spore size of

9

many fungi attacking herbaceous plants may be related to efficiency of impaction on stems and leaves.

Using a wind-tunnel Gregory (1951) has studied the impaction on vertical cylinders of spores of various sizes at winds of different speeds. Air flowing past a cylinder is deflected in streamlines around it, but particles in the air may have sufficient momentum to cut across the stream to some extent and impact on the cylinder (Fig. 3). It is found that efficiency

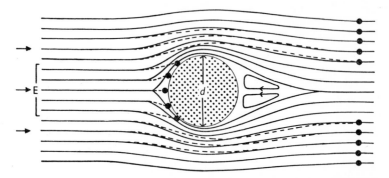

FIG. 3. Streamlines of air (continuous lines) and particle trajectories (dashed lines) around a cylindrical obstruction (seen in plan). E, streamlines carrying spores towards cylinder; *d*, diameter of cylinder; arrows on left show direction of wind. Particles indicated by large black dots. After Gregory (1961).

of impaction increases directly with spore size and wind velocity, and inversely with cylinder width. The general principles of impaction hold also for objects of shape other than cylindrical.

Gregory found that the very small spores of the giant puffball (*Calvatia gigantea*) were not impacted at all on any of his cylinders with the wind velocities used, but that the large spores of the club-moss *Lycopodium* were freely deposited. A consideration of the efficiency of impaction led him to recognize certain spores as essentially 'impactors'. He pointed out that the spores of many stem and leaf parasites (such as the conidia of Erysiphales, the sporangia (conidia) of Peronosporales, the uredospores of rusts, and the conidia of *Helminthosporium*) being relatively large are good impactors. He noted further (Gregory, 1961) that the giant ascospores of the lichen *Pertusaria pertusa* (Fig. 4) would impact with reasonable efficiency on a tree-trunk, the normal habitat for this species. On the other hand

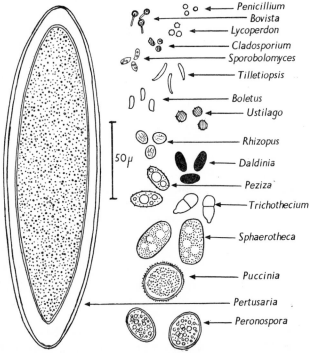

FIG. 4. Some air-borne fungal spores belonging to the following species: *Penicillium italicum, Bovista plumbea, Lycoperdon perlatum, Cladosporium herbarum, Sporobolomyces roseu, Tilletiopsis minor, Boletus granulatus, Ustilago avenae, Rhizopus stolonifer, Daldinia concentrica, Peziza badia, Trichothecium roseum, Sphaerotheca pannosa, Puccinia obtegens, Peronospora parasitica, Pertusaria pertusa.*

the spores of soil fungi (such as *Penicillium, Aspergillus, Mucor,* and *Trichoderma*) tend to be relatively small and are, therefore, poor impactors. They are probably normally brought to earth by rain-wash.

Finally spore size may be considered in relation to germination. If a stem or leaf parasite is to succeed in infecting its host, or if a soil fungus is to establish itself in competition with other soil organisms, not only must germination occur but it must also be effective. Here the 'inoculation potential' of a spore is probably significant and this will be influenced by the amount of the food reserve, itself probably roughly proportional to the size of the spore. The importance of this factor is, however, difficult to assess and an experimental approach is hard to envisage.

In considering the possible adaptive significance of the size of a spore, it is probably impossible to locate with any degree of certainty the episode in a spore's life in connexion with which selection pressure has really made itself felt. Indeed, size in any one instance is probably a compromise between competing tendencies, and in a great many airborne fungi a more or less spherical spore about 10 μ in diameter has resulted.

There are a number of fungi in which spores are regularly spread by insects and in some of these spore size may be related to this particular kind of dispersal, especially where flies (Diptera) are regularly involved and the spores are drawn into the insect through suctorial mouth-parts. In these cases the spores are smooth-walled, mixed with sugary slime and consistently minute. Three outstanding examples, widely scattered taxonomically, are the basidiospores of Phallales (e.g. *Phallus impudicus*), the conidia of ergot (*Claviceps purpurea*), and the pycnidiospores (spermatia) of rusts.

Just as selective pressures on spore size may be envisaged as operating in connexion with any episode of a spore's life, so these pressures may have affected spore shape.

A suggested example, associated with take-off, relates to ascospore form (Ingold, 1954). It has been pointed out that in those Discomycetes and Pyrenomycetes in which spores are violently discharged there is a considerable range in the shape of the ascospores. In the great majority the upper half (that nearer the apex of the ascus) is usually the mirror image of the lower. This type may be termed 'bipolar symmetrical'. However, in many species, distributed widely taxonomically, a transverse cut at the mid-point between the two ends of the spore would divide it into a relatively large and blunt upper part, and a relative small lower part with a sharper end (Fig. 5). This is the 'bipolar asymmetrical' type. The interesting fact is that the opposite condition, with a sharper apex and a blunter base, never seems to occur. Since no development factors would appear to be responsible, it is reasonable to explore a 'teleological' explanation.

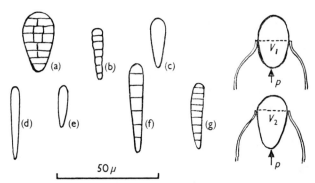

Fig. 5. Left: bipolar asymmetrical ascospores. Lichens: (a) *Arthothelium spectabile*, (b) *Sclerophyton circumscriptum*, and (c) *Thrombium epigaeum* (after Lorrain Smith). Discomycetes: (d) *Scleroderris ribesia*, (e) *Helotium fructigenum*, (f) *Lecanidion atratum*, and (g) *Cryptodiscus pellidus* (after Boudier). Right: diagram of spores escaping from ascus; V, volume below dotted line; $V_2 > V_1$; p = hydrostatic pressure.

Bipolar asymmetrical ascospores are formed only in Inoperculate Ascomycetes. In these successive discharge of ascospores takes place through a narrow apical pore in the ascus, although the interval between the escape of sister spores may often be very small.

We may consider what happens during the escape of a spore. As it is being pushed through the pore and is stretching it wider, it will probably be moving very slowly and when the stretched pore is grasping the spore at its widest part, its velocity is likely to be zero or nearly so. The work done thereafter by the hydrostatic pressure of the ascus is directed towards the discharge of the spore and not towards stretching the pore. This work is given by pV, where p is the hydrostatic pressure and V the volume of the part of the spore immersed in the ascus sap at this stage. Assuming the friction between spore and pore to be of negligible magnitude, pV can be equated to $\frac{1}{2}mv^2$ where m is the mass of the spore and v its initial velocity on discharge. If this reasoning is correct, it is clear that for spores of equal mass, the nearer the widest part is to the front end, the greater V and, therefore, all else being equal, the greater the initial velocity and hence the distance of discharge (Fig. 5). The higher the spore is shot the greater its chance of effective dispersal. Quite apart from the effect suggested above, the spore with bipolar asymmetry is to some extent streamlined. Air resistance is probably reduced as compared with a symmetrical type of equal mass and with a given initial velocity of discharge the throw may thus be increased.

Selection might also be expected to operate on the form of of the spore particularly if the rate of fall in still air is a significant factor in aerial dispersal.

The mathematics of fall of ellipsoidal particles have recently been studied rather fully by Dr. Fonda† and the results of some of his findings are illustrated in Fig. 6. The rate of settling depends on orientation which tends to remain unaltered during fall. The mean rate for randomly oriented ellipsoidal particles, however, is always less than for spherical ones of the same volume, and decreases as the particles become more elongated. Consequently if the velocity of fall is an important factor in aerial dispersal, selection might favour the elongated spore.

It might be assumed that sometimes the form of a spore is of significance in relation to deposition. However, there has been no study of the deposition of, for example, elongated spores as compared with spherical ones so far as the air spora is concerned. Nevertheless, a study of the spora of certain aquatic habitats strongly suggests that the problem of impaction has been to the fore in moulding spore form.

Growing on submerged leaves of deciduous trees and shrubs

† Personal communication reporting work done under the aegis of the National Coal Board.

decaying in the beds of well-aerated streams is a clearly-defined and apparently world-wide flora of aquatic Hyphomycetes, a major group of Fungi Imperfecti (Ingold, 1942 and 1959). The mycelium of these fungi ramifies in the leaf tissue,

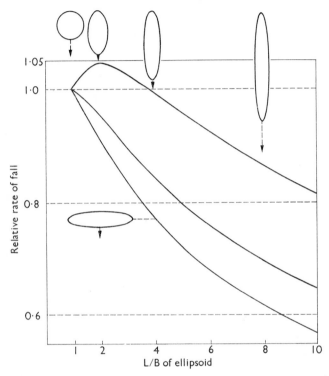

Fɪɢ. 6. Relative rates of fall of ellipsoids with the two short axes equal and all of same volume. Uppermost curve, long axis vertical; lowest curve, a short axis vertical; middle curve, mean terminal vertical component of randomly oriented ellipsoids. All related to a sphere of same volume with a rate of fall of 1·0. From tables compiled by Dr. A. Fonda.

particularly in the veins and petioles, and the conidiophores project, liberating their spores into the water. The whole story of dispersal—spore production, transport, and deposition—takes place below water. The outstanding feature of these organisms is that spores are not usually spherical or oblong, like

15

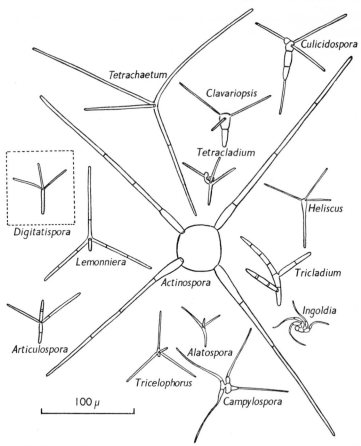

Fig. 7. Spores of aquatic Hyphomycetes (and, in dashed square, the basidiospore of *Digitatispora marina*). The following species are figured: *Actinospora megalospora, Alatospora acuminata, Articulospora tetracladia, Campylospora chaetocladia, Clavariopsis aquatica, Culicidospora aquatica, Heliscus tentaculus, Ingoldia craginiformis, Lemonniera aquatica, Tetrachaetum elegans, Tetracladium marchalianum, Tricladium splendens, Triscelophorus monosporus.*

those of most terrestrial fungi, but for the most part are either long or thread-like or, more commonly, branched structures. Further when the spore is branched it most often takes the form of four long arms diverging from or from near a common point: the spore is tetraradiate (Fig. 7). In a stream cakes of foam commonly collect in eddies or against barriers of twigs particularly below small waterfalls. The foam acts as a very efficient spore trap collecting the spores of these aquatic fungi in large numbers. If this foam is examined microscopically a very clear picture is obtained of the remarkable water spora.

When the development story of species with tetraradiate spores is followed, it is evident that this type of spore may be formed in very different ways. The spores shown in Fig. 7 all belong clearly to different genera. It would be tedious to describe the developmental process in each, but this is illustrated for two highly contrasted genera in Fig. 8. Suffice to say that in some the spore is attached to its conidiophore by the tip of one of the four arms (in *Clavariopsis, Heliscus, Alatospora, Tetrachaetum, Tetracladium*, and *Articulospora*) whilst in others attachment is near the point of divergence of the arms (*Lemonniera, Triscelophorus, Actinospora, Campylospora*). In some the spore is a terminal thallospore or aleuriospore (*Clavariopsis, Tetrachaetum, Articulospora, Tetracladium, Triscelophorus, Ingoldia*, and *Actinospora*), but in others (*Heliscus, Alatospora, Lemonniera*) it is a phialospore. In some the four arms develop simultaneously from a spherical primordium (in *Lemonniera* and *Actinospora*); in others the arms arise in succession (*Tetracladium, Articulospora, Triscelophorus*); in still others there is a first-formed arm from the apex of which three others arise simultaneously (*Clavariopsis, Heliscus*); whilst in *Tetrachaetum, Culicidospora*, and *Alatospora* two arms are formed by a main axis bent in the middle and at the elbow the other two arms develop as lateral outgrowths.

Considering the extraordinary diversity in the mode of development of the tetraradiate spore in these aquatic fungi, it is difficult to resist the conclusion that there is here a striking case of parallel evolution and that this kind of spore has some special advantages in the aquatic environment. When these advantages are considered there are two obvious possibilities. First a tetraradiate spore might settle relatively slowly in water and hence would stand a better chance of being carried some distance before coming to rest. This explanation is in keeping with the concept that in planktonic algae long spines are of value in retarding sedimentation. Secondly there is the possibility that a tetraradiate spore behaves as a minute anchor and so stands a better chance of arrest on a suitable

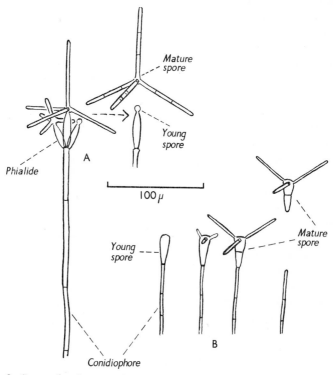

FIG. 8. Spore development in two aquatic Hyphomycetes. A, *Lemonniera aquatica*, conidiophore with three phialides each bearing a spore at a different stage of development; the central phialide is also shown later after one spore has been shed and another has just begun to form. B, *Clavariopsis aquatica*, stages in spore development and final liberation.

substratum. This explanation seems more likely than one based on the value of retarded sedimentation. The spores of these fungi have a density only very slightly greater than 1·0, so that their rate of fall in still water is very small. This has been determined (Webster, 1959) as about 0·1 mm per second. Tetraradiate spores (e.g. of *Clavariopsis aquatica*, *Tetrachaetum elegans*, *Tetracladium marchalianum*) do not settle more slowly than spores of a more usual form (e.g. those of *Margaritispora aquatica* and *Dactylella aquatica*). It is to be noted that a rate of fall of 0·1 mm per second is insignificant in relation to the rate of flow in most streams. Indeed, if retarding devices are called for at all, these would be much more likely to arise in elements of the air spora, where the difference in density between spore and transporting medium is great, than in the water spora.

A similar story can be developed for the greatly elongated spores which are a feature of some of the aquatic Hyphomycetes. In these species the spores are C or S shaped with the curvature occupying more than a single plane. In this case also it can be argued that the form of these spores is primarily of value in relation to anchorage.

Webster (1959) has made an experimental study of the impaction of spores of aquatic Hyphomycetes on cylinders exposed in a 'water-tunnel'. The work closely parallels that of Gregory on aerial spores using a wind-tunnel. Webster used species with tetraradiate spores, others with filiform spores and also *Dactylella aquatica* with spores of a more conventional form which are almost ellipsoidal with dimensions 30 × 40 μ. He concluded that 'in general the tetraradiate spore is more efficiently trapped than any other spore type with which it has been compared', probably because of the three-point contact which such a spore makes on impact with an under-water object.

If branched tetraradiate spores are generally to be interpreted as responses to the aquatic environment, it might be expected that they would occur in other groups of aquatic fungi. It is, therefore, of interest that in the marine fungus *Digitatispora marina*, the only basidiomycete known to produce its hymenium below water, the basidiospores are tetraradiate (Fig. 7) and in some of the marine Ascomycetes (e.g. *Halosphaeria quadricornuta*) ascospores of this type are found. Outside the fungi altogether, the tetraradiate aquatic type of propagule is found as a regular means of vegetative propagation in certain species of the seaweed *Sphacelaria* (e.g. *S. fusca*).

FORM AND FUNCTION OF FUNGAL SPORES

REFERENCES

BULLER, A. H. R. (1909). *Researches on Fungi* Vol. I. London.

CALLAGHAN, A. A. (1962). Observations on perithecium production and spore discharge in *Pleurage setosa*. *Trans. Br. mycol. Soc.* **45,** 249–254.

GREGORY, P. H. (1945). The dispersion of air-borne spores. *Trans. Br. mycol. Soc.* **36,** 46–51.

—— (1951). Deposition of airborne *Lycopodium* spores on cylinders. *Ann. appl. Biol.* **38,** 357–376.

—— (1961). *The microbiology of the atmosphere.* London.

INGOLD, C. T. (1942). Aquatic Hyphomycetes of decaying alder leaves. *Trans. Br. mycol. Soc.* **25,** 339–417.

—— (1954). Ascospore form. *Trans. Br. mycol. Soc.* **37,** 19–21.

—— (1959). Submerged aquatic Hyphomycetes. *J. Quekett microsc. Club* Ser. 4, **5,** 115–130.

SCHRÖDTER, H. (1960). Dispersal by air and water—the flight and landing. Chapter 6 in *Plant Pathology:* an Advanced Treatise, Vol. 3. by J. G. Horsfall and A. E. Dimond. New York, 169–227.

SREERAMULU, T. and RAMALINGAM, A. (1961). Experiments on the dispersion of *Lycopodium* and *Podaxis* spores in the air. *Ann. appl. Biol.* **49,** 659–670.

STEPANOV, K. M. (1935). (Dissemination of infective diseases of plants by air currents—in Russian, English title.) *Bull. Pl. Prot. Leningr.* Ser. 2. Phytopath., No. 8., 1–68.

WEBSTER, J. (1959). Experiments with spores of aquatic hyphomycetes. I Sedimentation and impaction on smooth surfaces. *Ann. Bot.* **23,** 595–611.

II

SPORE LIBERATION
IN MUCORALES†

A CENTRAL theme of this book is that the solution of dispersal problems has had a great impact on the structure of fungi and, therefore, in trying to understand structure, its relationship to spore dispersal should be constantly in mind. In the present chapter this attitude is developed in connexion with a single distinctive order of Lower Fungi.

Mucorales, with about 45 genera and some 275 species, seems a really 'natural' group of essentially terrestrial fungi. The mycelium is well-developed and non-septate when young. Asexual reproduction is typically by non-motile spores produced in sporangia, or if conidia are formed instead of, or in addition to, sporangia, they can reasonably be interpreted as the ultimate stage in sporangium reduction. The asexual spores are normally raised above the substratum on erect sporangiophores or conidiophores. Further the group is characterized by a fairly distinctive sexual process resulting in zygospore formation.

The general biology of Mucorales is interesting. Many are soil saprophytes, especially species of *Mucor, Mortierella, Absidia, Cunninghamella,* and *Syncephalastrum.* Some occur with great regularity on the dung of larger herbivores. Thus in the early phases of the succession on horse-dung species of *Mucor, Pilaria,* and especially *Pilobolus* normally appear. Some members of the order develop on the droppings of smaller rodents such as field mice. These fungi include saprophytes belonging to the genera *Mucor, Phycomyces, Thamnidium, Helicostylum, Coemansia, Kickxella, Mortierella,* and *Haplosporangium.* Both on horse- and on mouse-dung the saprophytic species are normally attacked at a later stage by parasitic members of the same order

† Based largely on Ingold and Zoberi (1963).

distributed amongst a number of genera: *Chaetocladium*, *Pipto-cephalis*, *Syncephalis*, *Dispira*, and *Dimargaris*. However, in these coprophilous Mucorales the distinction between parasites and saprophytes is not always easy to draw. In most species of *Piptocephalis* parasitism seems to be practically obligate, but others, for example the common *Chaetocladium brefeldii*, grow and sporulate readily on nutrient agar, but are probably always parasitic in nature.

Both the saprophytic and the parasitic Mucorales of dung appear to have the same dispersal story. The spores are eaten incidentally with food and, having passed through the alimentary canal, germinate subsequently in the excrement. It is interesting to note how varied is the fungus flora of the droppings of field mice. In a recent brief examination of mouse pellets in the author's own garden, thirteen genera of Mucorales regularly developed. It is difficult to resist the impression that members of the order reach their fullest expression on this unlikely substratum. The mucoraceous flora on mouse dung is distinctly richer in species than that on horse dung. However, species of *Pilobolus*, such a striking feature of the early coprophilous succession on horse dung, seem to be rare on the dung of field mice.

Another biological group in Mucorales consists of species found on the larger fungi. *Syzygites megalocarpus* (= *Sporodinia grandis*) is a common mould on a wide range of decaying agarics. The much rarer *Dicranophora fulva* has been found only on *Paxillus*, *Gomphidius*, and *Boletus*, now generally regarded as closely related toadstool genera. Species of *Spinellus* are common on *Mycena* and *Collybia* and are probably parasitic.

Some Mucorales are unspecialized parasites of the sappy tissues of higher plants. Thus *Rhizopus stolonifer* commonly causes a soft-rot of fruit such as apples, plums, and tomatoes; in the warmer countries *Choanephora cucurbitarum* brings about decay in the flowers and fruit of cucurbits; and *Gilbertella persicaria* is responsible for a dry-rot in peaches.

Finally, rather sharply separated from other Mucorales, are the hypogeal fungi grouped in Endogonaceae, a family closely parallel to Tuberales in Ascomycetes and to Hymenogastrales in Basidiomycetes. In *Endogone*, for example, the reproductive bodies (sporangia, zygospores, or chlamydospores) are usually aggregated into small but macroscopic sporophores and, as with truffles, dispersal is presumably by rodents which grub up and eat these fruit-bodies. Indeed, in North America the characteristic chlamydospores of *Endogone* have been found abundantly in the intestinal tracts of rodents (Dowding, 1955). The Endogonaceae will not, however, be considered further in this chapter.

Benjamin (1959) recognizes eleven families in Mucorales, but their interrelationships are more than usually dubious. However, from the functional rather than the systematic point of view four fairly distinct types of asexual apparatus seem to be involved. The best known is the large spherical or sub-spherical sporangium with a substantial columella and containing rarely less than a hundred and usually many thousand spores. In the relatively huge sporangia of *Phycomyces blakesleeanus* the number may reach 100000. Secondly, there is the sporangiole; a small nearly spherical sporangium with from two to about twenty spores and with the columella usually poorly developed. A third type is the merosporangium; really a cylindrical sporangiole containing from two to a dozen spores in a single row. Finally there are conidia. In certain species it is clear that they are to be interpreted as reduced sporangioles or reduced merosporangia. However, in others (e.g. species of *Cunninghamella*, *Mycotypha*, and *Chaetocladium*) the validity of this interpretation is by no means clear and it seems best, in general, to use the non-committal term 'conidium'. These four types will be considered in some detail.

In species with relatively large columellate sporangia three general arrangements can easily be recognized: those in which direct liberation into the air is unlikely because the spores are associated with sticky mucilage; those in which the spores form a dry friable mass on dehiscence of the sporangia so that they are readily blown away; and species of *Pilobolus* in which the whole sporangium is violently discharged.

Amongst the first group are some species where the spores are suspended in a mucilaginous matrix within a very thin

23

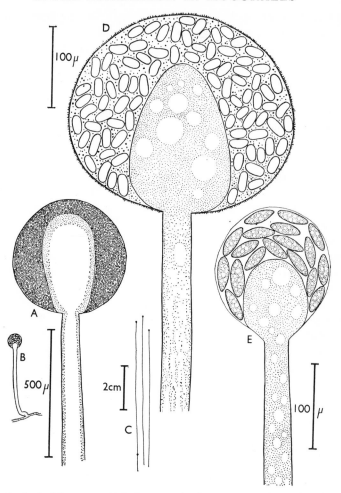

FIG. 9. A–C *Phycomyces blakesleeanus:* A, large sporangium; B, dwarf sporangiophore at same magnification; C, three sporangiophores. D, *Mucor plasmaticus.* E, *Spinellus fusiger.*

sporangium wall which, nevertheless, persists until it is ruptured by some external influence. To this sub-division *Phycomyces*, *Spinellus*, and some of the larger species of *Mucor* (e.g. *M. plasmaticus*) belong (Fig. 9). Of special interest is *Phycomyces*,

24

the commonest species being *P. nitens*. This has been isolated on many occasions nearly always from the droppings of rats and mice. A closely similar but apparently rare species, *P. blakesleeanus*, has been used extensively as a laboratory organism in nutritional and physiological work. In both of these species the steel-grey sporangiophores are unbranched, strongly phototropic and may reach a height of 20 cm.

A remarkable feature of *Phycomyces* may be noted, namely its ability to form its sporangiophores even when the humidity of the air is maintained at a very low level. If spores are sown in specimen tubes (2·5 × 2·5 cm) brimful with malt agar, and some are placed in a dessicator over anhydrous calcium chloride whilst others are over water, the sporangiophores are produced equally freely under both conditions, whereas parallel cultures of *Mucor*, for example, produce no aerial growth over the dessicant. This ability of *Phycomyces* seems to be due to the impermeable nature of the mature wall of the sporangiophore practically restricting evaporation to the narrow growing zone just below the sporangium, and to the well-developed transpiration stream making good such water as is lost. If an opened Petri dish culture of *Phycomyces* is examined under the low power of the microscope, the rapidly flowing contents in the principal hyphae are easily seen, and if a particular stream is followed it always leads into the base of a sporangiophore. This streaming depends on transpiration and the hyphal contents flow to the site of water loss.

With such a striking ability to erect long aerial sporangiophores in dry air, it is remarkable that the sporangium does not liberate dry spores. Had this ability been coupled with a sporangial apparatus like that of *Rhizopus*, *Phycomyces* might well be a much more abundant organism.

It is worthy of note that very long phototropic sporangiophores seem to be a feature of certain other coprophilous Mucorales especially *Mucor mucedo*, *M. plasmaticus*, and *Pilaria anomala*. The growth of these long sporangiophores may, perhaps, be regarded as a step in dispersal.

As pointed out by Dobbs (1939) the sporangium in a number of the commonest species of *Mucor* (e.g. *M. hiemalis* and

25

M. ramannianus) is converted at maturity into a sporangial drop. The sporangium wall seems to dissolve (it is said to be 'diffluent') except for a basal region which persists as a minute collar round the columella (Fig. 10). Ordinarily in Petri dish cultures

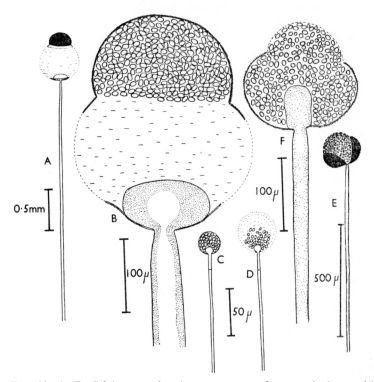

FIG. 10. A, B, *Pilaira anomala:* A, upper part of sporangiophore with dehisced sporangium now forming a sporangial drop; B, similar sporangial drop (vert. opt. sect.). C, D, *Mucor ramannianus:* C, undehisced sporangium; D, sporangium now converted into a sporangial drop. E, F, *Gilbertella persicaria:* E, sporangiophore with dehisced sporangium and slimy drop of spores exuding; F, similar sporangial drop (vert. opt. sect.).

the sporangial drop is several times the volume of the original sporangium. On exposure to dry air, however, the drop, which apparently contains mucilage, evaporates leaving the spores firmly cemented to one another and the columella. Strong air currents or vigorous tapping of cultures fail to dislodge the spores. This kind of sporangial behaviour is also seen in *Dicranophora fulva* and in the terminal sporangia of *Thamnidium elegans* and *Helicostylum fresenii*. A slight modification of the basal pattern is to be found in *Gilbertella persicaria* (Fig. 10) a member of the Choanephoraceae. The sporangium wall is persistent, but dehiscence is by a line of weakness running from pole to pole around the spherical sporangium. It seems that the sporangium contains, intermixed with the spores, mucilage which swells, perhaps by absorbing water through the columella, thus pushing apart the two halves of the wall. In this fungus the polar bristles on the spores characteristic of the family occur, but they are too fine to be seen with the light microscope.

Pilaira anomala also produces a sporangial drop (Fig. 10). In *Pilaira* and *Pilobolus*, the only two genera of the family Pilobolaceae, the sporangium is highly distinctive. Its wall is differentiated into an upper resistant blackened part and a lower delicate semi-transparent part which is white in reflected light. Within are spores and mucilage, the spores being concentrated in the upper part. In both genera the mature sporangium ruptures in the delicate region of the wall around a circle of latitude well below the equator of the sporangium.

Pilaira anomala is a common coprophilous species occurring very early in the succession on horse dung. After sporangial dehiscence the mucilage swells considerably, presumably by absorption of water through the large columella, and is directly exposed in the gap created by dehiscence. Thus a sporangial drop is formed and this may be carried onto the herbage around the dung by the growth of the unbranched phototropic sporangiophore which elongates from a few millimetres to several centimetres in a few hours. When the delicate sporangiophores wither, the sporangia, without their columellas, are left adhering to the grass just as if they had been discharged there (Fig. 11).

The sporangial drop is an example of the 'stalked spore-drop', a distinctive type of spore-presentation mechanism probably associated most often with insect dispersal or rain-splash. As

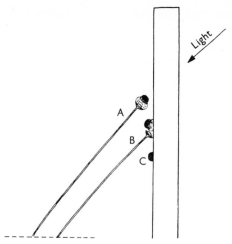

Fig. 11. *Pilaria anomala.* Diagram of how a sporangium, carried to a neighbouring object (here a vertical sheet of glass) by elongation of the sporangiophore, becomes attached so that the black cap covers the spores. A, sporangiophore growing towards light. B, similar sporangiophore in which the sporangium has touched the glass and become stuck. C, a deposited sporangium has become firmly cemented to the glass and its sporangiophore has withered.

will appear later, it is found amongst Mucorales also in some merosporangiferous genera and in Kickxellaceae. Further, outside the order this kind of apparatus is encountered repeatedly.

Figure 12 illustrates some examples. In *Dipodascus* the stalk is an empty ascus and the drop consists of the escaped ascospores and sap. In *Cephaloascus* the stalk is a diploid ascophore and the drop is a mass of spores derived from the deliquescence of a head of asci. In *Ceratocystis* the stalk is the neck of a perithecium and the drop consists of extruded ascospores. In *Gliocladium* the conidiophore is of the *Penicillium* type but the phialospores, being produced with slime, form a drop, and *Graphium* is similar but the stalk is a sheaf of parallel hyphae. In *Dictyostelium*, probably not placeable in the Fungi at all, the stalk is a cellulose tube stuffed with inflated encysted amoebae and the drop is composed of spores or cysts in a fluid matrix.

In certain species, not only of *Mucor* but also of some closely related genera, especially *Rhizopus*, *Actinomucor*, and *Circinella*, the spores are not associated with mucilage in the sporangium; dehiscence by rupture of the wall takes place and direct aerial dispersal is possible. A good example is *M. petrinsularis* (Fig. 13). The ripe unburst sporangium is packed with spores which, being closely confined between the sporangium wall and the

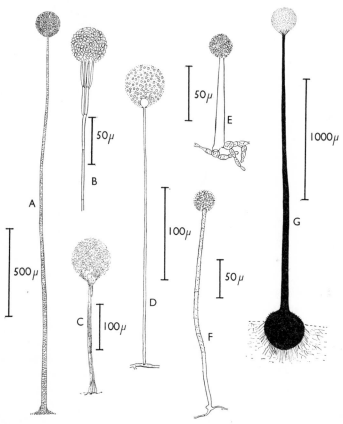

FIG. 12. A, *Dictyostelium discoideum;* B, *Gliocladium roseum;* C, *Graphium cuneiferum;* D, *Mucor ramannianus;* E, *Dipodascus uninucleatus;* F, *Cephaloasus fragans;* G, *Ceratocystis adiposa.* All, except *Ceratocytis*, shown in longitudinal section.

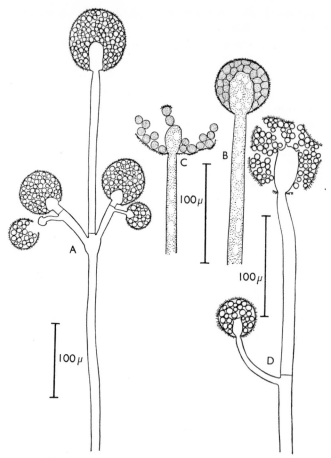

FIG. 13. A, *Actinomucor elegans:* part of sporangiophore; one lateral sporangium has just separated from its columella. B, C, *Mucor petrinsularis:* intact sporangium and another after dehiscence under damp conditions. D, *M. plumbeus:* apical region of sporangiophore, the terminal sporangium has dehisced, the lateral one is still intact.

columella, are compressed into polyhedral shapes, a condition not common in mucoraceous sporangia. As the spores mature their tendency to round off increases and finally the sporangium wall ruptures in a somewhat irregular manner to form a kind of saucer with most of the spores lying on its upper surface, although a few adhere to the columella. The wide opening of the sporangium, a special feature of this species, seems to be due to swelling of those spores which during development occupy the somewhat acute angle between the base of the columella and the sporangial wall. Dehiscence of the sporangium occurs under conditions of saturation and is not related to drying. If a young sporulating culture on nutrient agar in a closed Petri dish is inverted and tapped, many spores drop on to the inner surface of the lid, mostly in groups each attached to a segment of sporangium wall.

The behaviour of the common species *M. plumbeus* is somewhat similar (Fig. 13). Under dry conditions the sporangium wall breaks into a few separate, angular fragments. Spores are readily dislodged on tapping an inverted culture or under the influence of a sufficient wind. Usually each wall fragment carries a small load of spores, although some spores escape singly.

Actinomucor elegans, a frequent species of apparently worldwide distribution, behaves in a somewhat different manner (Fig. 13). This fungus is isolated from *Mucor* in a separate genus by virtue of its stoloniferous habit. In *A. elegans* the whole spore mass enclosed by the sporangial wall slips off the smallish columella and is dispersed as a whole. This release can be brought about either by wind or by mechanical agitation.

In some other mucoraceous moulds dry spores are liberated, mostly singly, when the sporangia dehisce on drying. A well-known example is *Rhizopus stolonifer* (Fig. 14). The mature sporangium is apophysate with a very large columella. On exposure to dry air this collapses in a striking and very definite manner so that it looks like an inverted pudding bowl balanced on the end of a stick represented by the relatively short deflated but stiff sporangiophore. Apparently at the same time, and possibly as a consequence of columella collapse, the brittle sporangial wall breaks into many small angular fragments. These with the dry spores form a powder easily blown away. Any mycologist is aware of the trouble caused by *Rhizopus stolonifer* if cultures are left around in the laboratory. It crops up as an unwanted contaminant everywhere, whereas most species of *Mucor* (e.g. *M. hiemalis* and *M. ramannianus*) never cause any trouble of this kind. The difference is related essentially to the different modes of spore liberation in those fungi.

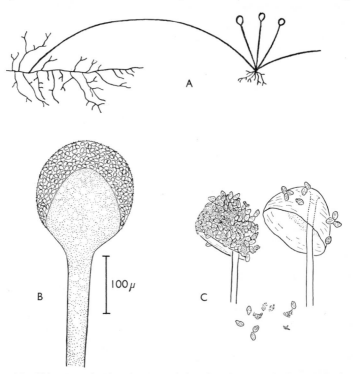

FIG. 14. *Rhizopus stolonifer.* A, an aerial stolon from behind the growing margin of a culture on agar has made contact with the medium again and produced a group of three sporangiophores and a system of rhizoidal hyphae; B, a sporangium in longitudinal section; C, Two sporangia which have dried and their columellas have collapsed; in one the load of dry wall fragments and spores is still intact, in the other they have mostly been blown away.

As in *Rhizopus stolonifer* so in *Circinella umbellata* (Fig. 15), and probably in other species of the genus, spores are shed dry and mostly singly. The sporangial wall breaks down on drying along a few irregular radial fractures exposing the spores which

32

sift away. A dry-spore mechanism also occurs in *Syzygites megalocarpus* (Fig. 15). The sporangiophore, which may be several centimetres long, branches dichotomously and repeatedly in the apical region each ultimate ramulus bearing a

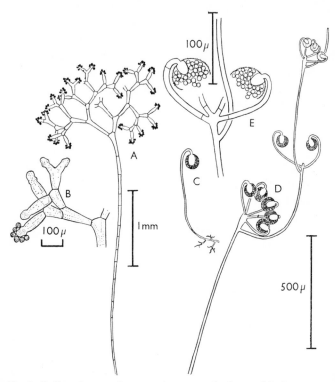

FIG. 15. A, B, *Syzygites megalocarpus:* A, sporangiophore with ripe sporangia, only part of unbranched stalk shown; B, part of branch system, one columella still has its layer of spores. C, D, E, *Circinella umbellata:* C, unbranched sporangiophore arising from feeding mycelium; D, usual type of sporangiophore with groups of sporangia and sympodial development; E, details of a sporangial group showing two dehisced sporangia.

small sporangium with a relatively large columella and a few rather big spores. At maturity the very thin sporangial walls completely disappear and the spores are left exposed on the columellas from which they are easily blown away.

33

It might be observed at this stage that, in spite of their abundance, mucoraceous moulds do not figure prominently in the air spora. An extensive aeromycological study has been made in Kansas, U.S.A. (Kramer *et al.*, 1959) lasting over two years and during this period Petri dishes with nutrient agar were exposed almost daily in an electrostatic bacterial air-sampler, the developing colonies being subsequently identified to the genus. Of 113667 colonies obtained, only 194 belonged to Mucorales and of these 156 were of *Rhizopus*. By way of contrast the figure for *Cladosporium* was 50548.

Pilobolus stands on its own as the only genus in Mucorales exhibiting violent spore discharge. It has attracted attention since it was first figured and crudely described towards the end of the seventeenth century. The history of research on *Pilobolus* and its general biology was fully summarized by Buller in the sixth volume of his Researches published in 1933. But since that time it has continued to attract research workers particularly in relation to its specialized nutrition, its phototropism and the periodicity of its sporangial discharge. This last subject will be discussed in a later chapter, and it is sufficient here to note its diurnal rhythm of ripening and discharge under natural conditions.

Pilobolus is a genus of about half a dozen species several of which are common. On horse dung the most abundant is *P. kleinii*, but *P. sphaerosporus* seems to be an easier species to grow and maintain in pure culture in the laboratory. The developmental story is illustrated in Fig. 16. From an intercalary carotene-rich 'trophocyst', delimited by cross-walls from the feeding mycelium, the sporangiophore arises as an erect phototropic aerial hypha. From the apex of this a sporangium is produced which is ultimately cut off by a highly arched cross-wall forming a substantial columella. Later the region of the sporangiophore immediately below swells to form the subsporangial bulb. At maturity the sporangium, which has essentially the same structure as that of *Pilaira*, undergoes dehiscence along a subequatorial line prior to violent discharge (Fig. 17). The mature sporangiophore, including its parent trophocyst, is a single turgid cell. The stretched cell-wall has

34

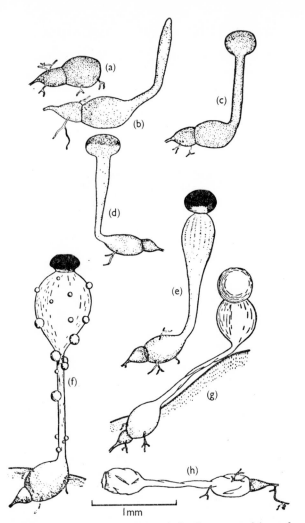

FIG. 16. *Pilobolus kleinii.* Daily cycle of development: (a) oval, orange trophocyst found in forenoon; (b) bright yellow, aerial hypha (sporangiophore) developed from trophocyst (3–5 p.m.); (c) swelling of tip of hypha to form sporangium (6–8 p.m.); (d) massing of contents in upper part of sporangial swelling (8–10 p.m.); (e) sporangium, with its black cap, formed and delimited from sporangiophore; subsporangial bulb beginning to swell (about midnight); (f) mature sporangiophore but sporangium not yet dehisced (8–11 a.m.); (g) sporangiophore immediately after bursting and exuding a drop of liquid; (h) deflated sporangiophore some hours after bursting showing the circular line of rupture. All drawn to approximately the same scale.

35

a lining layer of protoplasm. This layer is considerably thicker just below the subsporangial bulb and in most species this region is rich in oil droplets containing carotene giving it a conspicuous orange colour particularly in *P. kleinii*. The large vacuole is occupied by cell sap with an osmotic pressure of about seven atmospheres (Buller, 1933).

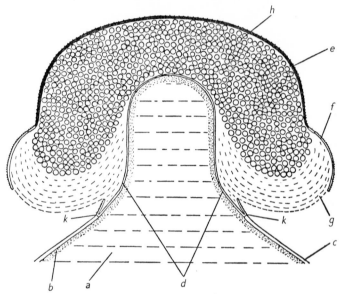

FIG. 17. *Pilobolus longipes*. Diagram of dehisced sporangium just before discharge. *a*, sporangiophore sap; *b*, layer of protoplasm; *c*, sporangiophore wall; *d*, columella; *e*, opaque black sporangial wall; *f*, semitransparent part of sporangium wall; *g*, mucilage; *h*, spores; *k*, region where sporangiophore ruptures.

Like the young sporangiophore, the mature structure is also positively phototropic: Buller regarded the upper part as an ocellus or simple eye. According to him the crystal-clear bulb formed a lens focusing light on the orange protoplasm below which acted as a retina. If this was not symmetrically illuminated differential growth just below the bulb occurred until the retina was again evenly lighted. It is to be noted, however, that there is no proof that carotene acts as a photo-receptor in connexion with the growth responses of fungi; indeed at present the balance of evidence rather suggests riboflavin.

It has been seen that the mature sporangium undergoes dehiscence and in the circular gap left the mucilage of the sporangium interior is fully exposed (Fig. 17). Shortly after dehiscene discharge takes place. This involves the rupture of the subsporangial bulb around a circular line just below the junction with the columella. Immediately this occurs the stretched wall of the sporangiophore contracts squirting out a drop of sap which carries the sporangium together with the columella to a distance of up to 2·5 metres.

The columella and the mucilage of the sporangium are freely wettable but the upper blackened part of the sporangial wall, studded with minute projecting crystals of calcium oxalate as in most species of *Mucor*, is unwettable and thus projects from the drop of sap. Further when the drop strikes an object, although the sporangium may momentarily be submerged, it bobs up again exposing the unwettable part. As a result when the sap and the mucilage dry the spore-mass, roofed over by the black resistant part of the sporangium wall, is completely protected and sticks fast. Discharged sporangia may remain thus for many days before the grass is eaten by a herbivore and the dispersal cycle completed by passage through the animal.

It is quite clear that *Pilaira* and *Pilobolus* resemble one another much more than either resembles any other genus of Mucorales, but there remains the fundamental difference that in one violent discharge occurs, whilst in the other it does not. In spite of the manifest pitfalls of phylogeny, it is difficult to refrain from posing the question: should *Pilaira* be considered an ancestral type, or close to an ancestral type, from which *Pilobolus* may have arisen, or is it a degenerate condition? It is difficult to envisage any evidence which might settle this problem. However, there is a suggestion that in its nutritional requirements *Pilobolus* is more exacting than *Pilaira* and, if this should prove to be so, *Pilaira* might more reasonably be considered the fore-runner of *Pilobolus* than a degenerate product of it.

Having considered spore-liberation in those Mucorales with large columellate sporangia, we may now pass on to consider the forms producing sporangioles. These are included in Thamnidiaceae and Choanephoraceae. In some, for example *Thamnidium elegans*, *Helicostylum fresenii* (Fig. 18) and *Choanephora trispora* (Fig. 20), sporangia as well as sporangioles occur, in others such as *Cokeromyces recurvatus* (Fig. 19) and *Radiomyces spectabilis* (Fig. 19) only sporangioles are produced. In all these fungi the sporangioles are deciduous and are easily blown off by wind. The sporangiole bears with it a length of stalk which is usually very short, but is relatively long in *Helicostylum piriforme* (Fig. 18). Most sporangioles are indehiscent. However, in *Choanephora trispora* the liberated sporangiole dehisces if it falls into water, its walls splitting into two hemispherical shells to liberate the spores with their polar bristles extended (Fig. 20). Again in *Radiomyces spectabilis* the sporangiole breaks down in water setting free its spores.

It should be emphasized that, although the sporangioles of *Thamnidium* and *Helicostylum* are deciduous, the sporangia behave in a different manner remaining attached and becoming converted into sporangial drops as in *Mucor hiemalis*.

Perhaps some of the sporangia in Mortierellaceae should be considered as sporangioles. In *Mortierella* there is no appreciable columella and some species have sporangia with very few spores and the number may even be reduced to one. However, these small sporangia do not appear to be deciduous. The same is true of *Haplosporangium bisporale* where the sporangia are regularly two-spored, but though so finely poised they are not apparently detachable by wind.

The merosporangiferous Mucorales have been reviewed in an outstanding monograph (Benjamin, 1959). Merosporangia are a feature of three families: Piptocephalidaceae, Syncephalastraceae, and Dimargaritaceae. In all merosporangia the sporangial wall breaks down at maturity so that a row of spores, sometimes called a 'spore-rod', is formed looking superficially like a chain of conidia; the chain being reduced to only two spores in Dimargaritaceae.

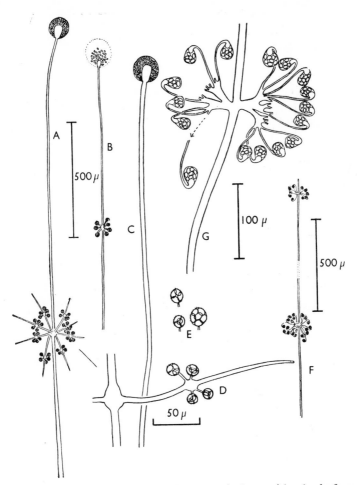

FIG. 18. A–E, *Helicostylum fresenii*: A, sporangiophore with whorl of spor-angiole-bearing branches; B, sporangiophore with whorl of sporangioles, terminal sporangium has become a sporangial drop; C, sporangiophore with terminal sporangium and no sporangioles; D, sporangiolar branch of A at higher magnification; E, liberated sporangioles. F, G, *H. piriforme*: F, sporangiophore, small straight section of sporangiophore between two whorls of sporangioles omitted; G, details of sporangiolar whorl, a single sporangiole just liberated is indicated.

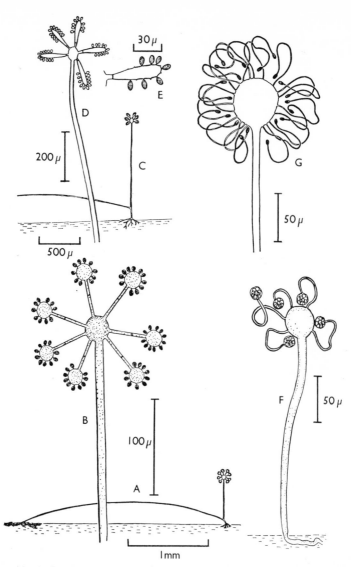

Fig. 19. A, B, *Radiomyces spectabilis:* A, stolon arising from feeding mycelium on agar producing sporangiophore near region of 'rooting'; B, details of sporangiophore. C–E, *R. embreei:* C, stolon producing conidiophore on agar near its point of 'rooting'; D, details of conidiophore; E, attachment of conidia to arm of conidiophore. F, *Cokeromyces recurvatus*, sporangiophore arising from feeding mycelium on agar. G, *C. poitrasii*, conidiophore head. B, D, F, and G in vert. opt. sect.

40

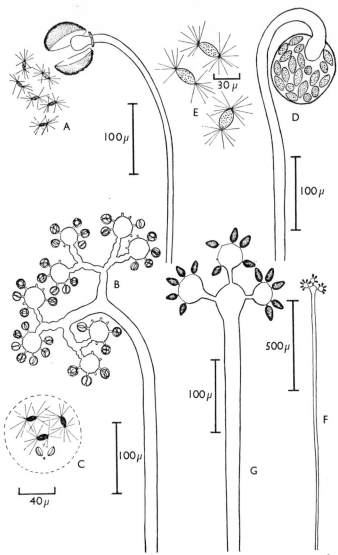

Fig. 20. A–C, *Choanephora trispora:* A, sporangiophore in water showing fracture of the wall and liberated spores; B, branched sporangiophore showing sporangioles attached to globose heads; C, a sporangiole which has fallen into a droplet of condensation water on the lid of an inverted Petri dish and has at once ruptured to liberate its three contained spores; the two halves of the old sporangiolar wall and its separated stalk also shown. D–G, *C. cucurbitarum:* D, "nodding" sporangium; E, liberated spores mounted in water; F, conidiophore; G, details of conidiophore apex. (B, D, and G in vert. opt. sect.).

In *Piptocephalis* (Fig. 21) the long sporangiophore is unbranched below but freely branched in a dichotomous manner in its upper regions. Each branch ends in a specialized 'head-cell' to which the merosporangia are attached. As noted by Benjamin (1959) two types of behaviour may occur. In the first (e.g. in *P. freseniana*) all the spore-rods from one head become involved in a single droplet of fluid, the identity of the individual rods being finally lost. Under the influence of a current of air the head-cells become detached, each carrying its spore-laden drop. In some other species (e.g. *P. virginiana*) the spore rods remain dry. When *P. virginiana* is subjected to a blast of air, some head-cells are blown off carrying their dry spore-rods, but individual rods are also detached and single spores may also become airborne (Ingold and Zoberi, 1963).

In *Syncephalis* the simple sporangiophore has a swollen apex from which radiating merosporangia arise. These may be directly attached but more commonly they occur two at a time on a basal cell. Sometimes the contents of this basal cell form what is effectively a spore, so that it seems that a V-shaped merosporangium is involved. This is so for example in *Syncephalis cordata*. In this, and probably in most if not all species of the genus, the head of the sporangiophore becomes involved in slime in which the sporangiospores, liberated by the breakdown of the merosporangial walls, are suspended (Fig. 22). In contrast the heads of *Syncephalastrum racemosum* remain dry and the radiating spore-rods are easily blown away (Fig. 22). Individual rods tend to remain intact, few spores escaping singly.

In Dimargaritaceae, characterized by two-spored merosporangia of hour-glass form, both spore-drop and dry-spore forms occur. In *Dimargaris crystalligena* the tall, unbranched sporangiophore has, as in *Syncephalis*, a globoid head. This bears radiating elongated cells, each the stalk-cell of a branch system. The spores in pairs, each representing a merosporangium, occur in whorls on the shorter, more distal cells of these systems. At maturity all the cells tend to separate from one another except for the large stalk-cells, and the whole head becomes involved in fluid. The result is a stalked spore-drop containing not only spores, which show a tendency to remain

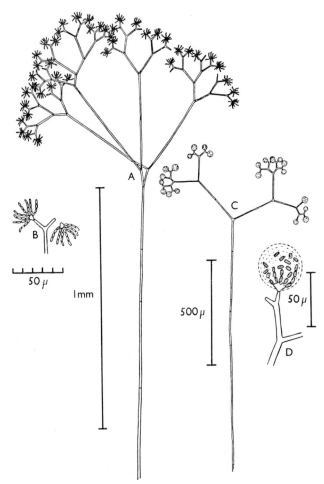

FIG. 21. A, B, *Piptocephalis virginiana:* A, sporangiophore bearing a tassel of dry-spore merosporangia at the tip of each ultimate branch; B, two head-cells with dry 'spore-rods' (merosporangia) attached; one head-cell has just separated. C, D, *P. freseniana:* C, a rather sparingly-branched sporangiophore with a sporangial drop at the end of each ramulus; D, part of the ultimate branching system with a single spore-drop in optical section.

43

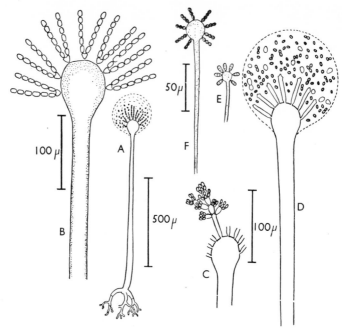

Fɪɢ. 22. A. B, *Syncephalis cordata:* A, sporangiophore with terminal spore-drop, spores shown black; B, apex of sporangiophore before break-up of the spore rods; the merosporangial walls have disappeared. C, D, *Dimargaris crystalligena:* C, part of apex of sporangiophore bearing sporangiferous branches; merosporangial walls have disappeared; D, later stage with spore-drop formed. E, F, *Syncephalastrum racemosum:* E, young sporangiophore with sporangia in which spores are differentiating; F, mature sporangiophore with dry spore-rods.

in the original pairs, but also the rounded-off cells of the merosporangiferous branch system (Fig. 22).†

Both the sporangiophores of *Syncephalis* and *Dimargaris* are further examples of the stalked-spore drop already discussed.

In contrast species of *Tieghemiomyces*, another genus of Dimargaritaceae, are dry-spore moulds. Two-spored merosporangia are borne in whorls on short, sparingly branched laterals arising at a height of 100–150 μ on an erect hyphae

† Dr. R. K. Benjamin (personal communication) has recently discovered two dry-spore species of *Dimargaris*.

44

which may be 500–1000 μ long. At maturity, as in other members of the family, the merosporangial walls break down leaving the spores in naked pairs. No slime is produced and the spores are readily blown away, although they tend to remain paired.

Benjamin has drawn attention to a very curious behaviour of the sporulating axis in both species of *Tieghemiomyces*. Immediately below the level of origin of the merosporangiferous branches, the cell of the main axis undergoes a transverse dehiscence. If the projecting part of the main axis is touched with a fine needle or a hair, the whole structure can be lifted off (Fig. 23). It appears that the axis is definitely sticky. This remarkable behaviour suggests that a special dispersal mechanism may be involved. *Tieghemiomyces* spp. are fungi of mouse dung. Perhaps in nature these sporulating systems are picked up by the whiskers of mice as they foray for food. Later, when the whiskers are cleaned, the spores may find their way into the alimentary tract.

In some Mucorales the conidial condition occurs. It seems to have arisen, by further reduction, from the sporangiolar and also possibly from the merosporangial condition. This seems clearly indicated by certain distinctive genera in which both sporangiolar and conidial species occur. Thus *Cokeromyces recurvatus* has sporangioles whilst in *C. poitrasii* conidia are produced, or, in other words, the sporangioles have become 1-spored (Fig. 19). Other precisely similar pairs are *Radiomyces spectabilis* and *R. embreei* (Fig. 19); and *Choanephora trispora* and *C. cucurbitarum* (Fig. 20). Further, the conidial fungus *Chaetocladium brefeldii* is classified in Thamnidiaceae because it looks as if it could fairly easily have been derived from such a spinose sporangiolar type as *Helicostylum fresenii*. The argument has been put forward that certain conidia are one-spored sporangioles, because two distinct walls can be recognized, an outer, the sporangiolar wall, and an inner, the actual spore wall. However, in evaluating this argument it must be remembered that many spores have two-ply walls. Sporangioles in Thamnidiaceae and Choanephoraceae on detachment carry a portion of the sporangiolar stalk. The fact that liberated

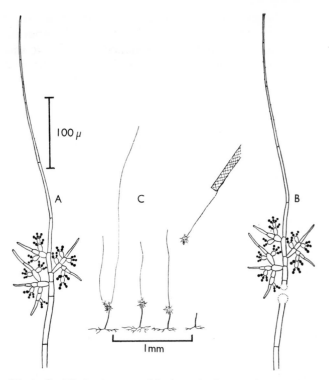

Fig. 23. A–C, *Tieghemiomyces californicus*. A, Sporangiophore (opt. long. sect.), the two spores of each merosporangium shown black; B, the same following rupture of the cell of the main axis below that from which the lowest sporangiferous branches arise, the free part of the sporangiophore has been lifted slightly and a drop of fluid is exuding from both segments of the ruptured cell; C, four sporangiophores arising from the feeding mycelium in agar, in that on the right the sticky projecting axis of the sporangiophore has been touched by a human hair (cross-hatched) and all but the stump has, in consequence, been lifted off.

conidia of *Choanephora*, *Cunninghamella*, and *Mycotypha* also have such stalks may, perhaps, be taken as supporting their sporangiolar nature.

Many conidial types are dry-spored and the conidia are easily blown away by wind. Clear-cut examples (Fig. 24) are *Chaetocladium* spp. *Cunninghamella* spp., *Mycotypha microspora*,

46

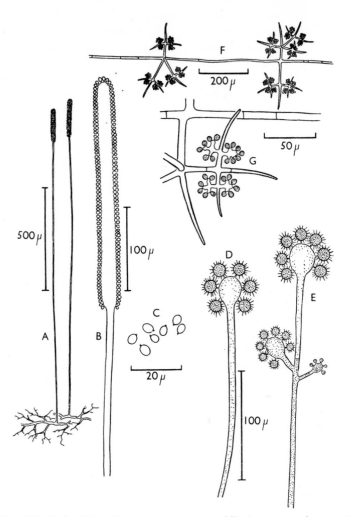

FIG. 24. A–C, *Mycotypha microspora*: A, conidiophores growing up from feeding mycelium on agar; B, head of conidiophore (vert. opt. sect.); C, liberated conidia. D,E, *Cunninghmella elegans*, two conidiophores (vert. opt. sect.). F,G, *Chaetocladium brefeldii*: F, part of horizontal conidiophore with lateral sporiferous branches; G, part of a branch more highly magnified, the spore-bearing structures in optical section.

47

Radiomyces embreei, and *Cokermyces poitrasii*. On the other hand, in most Kickxellaceae conidia at maturity become involved in fluid and are not wind-dispersed. In *Kickxella alabastrina* the conidiophore bears a terminal umbel of sporiferous branches each bearing on its upper surface several rows of closely set pseudophialides. Each of these gives rise to a single elongated spore. A drop of fluid is formed which embraces all the spores of an umbel and into this drop they may be liberated. The drop is held in the umbel rather like an egg in an egg-cup and does not encroach on the sporiferous branches which, like the pseudophialides, are unwettable. In *Coemansia* the individual spore-bearing branch carries its own droplet (Fig. 25).

Spirodactylon aureum, is a remarkable member of Kickxellaceae deserving special mention. According to Benjamin (1959) it is a dry-spore form. Like *Tieghemiomyces* it is reported from mouse dung and it is tempting to suggest again that the peculiar structure may be associated with mouse dispersal. The branched conidiophore has a rough spinose surface. At intervals there are spore-bearing regions, each in the form of a fairly tight helix, in which the spores on pseudophialides face inwards towards the longitudinal axis of the helix. The arrangement seems quite unsuited to normal aerial dispersal (Fig. 26). However, it might be envisaged that hairs or whiskers of a passing mouse might easily become temporarily involved with the spinous surface of the conidial apparatus. When the animal moved on, the helices might be pulled out to return with a spring to their former position jerking off the dry spores in the process.

It will be seen from this consideration of a relatively small but probably natural order of fungi that the asexual apparatus shows a consideral range of variation, and it seems that the problem of spore liberation is solved in a number of different ways in the various genera. Further in some forms closely similar in essential structure, spore liberation follows very different lines. The general moral that may be drawn from a contemplation of Mucorales is that in considering any spore-bearing structure in fungi, it is pertinent to ask the question: how exactly are the spores set free?

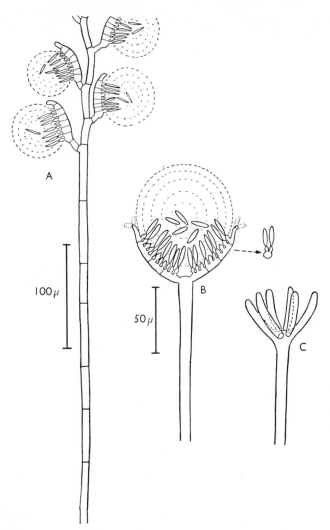

FIG. 25. A, *Coemansia guatemalensis:* upper part of conidiophore axis and lower part of fertile zone (long. sect.). B,C, *Kickxella alabastrina:* B, mature conidiophord (long. sect. through two sporiferous branches; form of branch tips in dotted outline and appearance of trans. sect. of a sporiferous branch indicated); C, young conidiophore with umbel of six developing sporiferous branches.

49

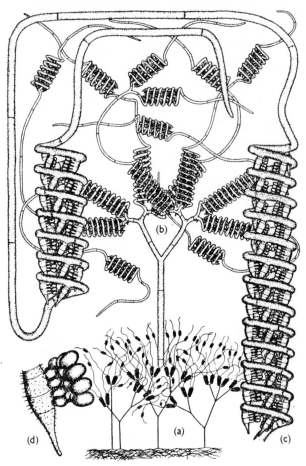

FIG. 26. *Spirodactylon aureum.* (a) Sketch of general habit of fruiting structures, ×15; (b) upper portion of conidiophore showing form of fertile branches, ×150; (c) portion at higher magnification, ×435; (d) small spore-bearing branch, directed inwards in the helix, showing conidia on pseudophialides, ×1575. After R. K. Benjamin (1959).

REFERENCES

BULLER, A. H. R. (1934). *Researches on Fungi VI.* London.
BENJAMIN, R. K. (1959). The merosporangiferous Mucorales. *Aliso* **4,** 321–433.

SPORE LIBERATION IN MUCORALES

Dobbs, C. G. (1939). 'Sporangial drops' in the Mucoraceae. *Nature Lond.* **143,** 286.

Dowding, E. S. (1955). *Endogone* in Canadian rodents. *Mycologia* **47,** 51–57.

Ingold, C. T. (1932). The sporangiophore of *Pilobolus*. *New Phyt.* **31,** 58–63.

—— (1939). *Spore discharge in land plants.* Oxford.

—— (1961). The stalked spore-drop. *New Phyt.* **60,** 181–183.

—— and Zoberi, M. H. (1963). The asexual apparatus of Mucorales in relation to spore liberation. *Trans. Br. mycol. Soc.* **46,** 115–134.

Kramer, C. L., Pady, S. M., Rogerson, C. T., and Ouye, L. G. Kanas Aeromycology II. Materials, methods and general results. *Trans. Kansas Acad. Sci.* 62, 184–199.

III

SPORE DISCHARGE IN *SORDARIA*

In this chapter an account is given of the process of spore liberation in *Sordaria fimicola* and of how it is influenced by external factors.

S. fimicola is a common fungus found on the dung of herbivorous animals such as horses, rabbits, and field mice. A number of closely similar species, *S. macrospora*, *S. humana*, and *S. destruens* have also been described. If many isolates of these four species are examined there appears to be considerable intergrading especially in respect of spore size and shape, the only characters on the basis of which species can be discriminated, and it seems quite likely that in reality only a single but rather variable species is involved (Callaghan, 1961).

S. fimicola is a convenient organism for experimental study because it grows quickly, and most isolates fruit abundantly on a suitable nutrient medium such as filter-paper-yeast-extract agar. Like most sordariaceous fungi, *S. fimicola* seems to require a supply of cellulose if perithecia are to be produced freely.

The structure of the perithecium is illustrated in Fig. 27. It is flask-shaped and contains an hymenium of asci in various stages of development. By the time spore-discharge commences paraphyses seem to have disappeared. The interior leads to the outside by a narrow neck-canal, ending in an ostiole, lined by re-curved periphyses. What little free space there is between and around the asci and in the neck-canal is occupied by mucilage. In *Sordaria*, and apparently in all active perithecia, no gas-phase occurs. The perithecium has at its tip a meristematic region so that for a time the neck slowly increases in length. Further it is positively phototropic. The result of this is that the spores are discharged towards the incident light.

It is of interest to note that in coprophilous fungi which discharge their spores violently positive phototropism is involved in aligning the spore gun. Conspicuous examples are

52

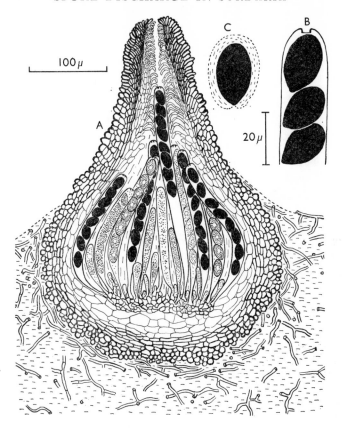

FIG. 27. *Sordaria fimicola*. A, longitudinal section of perithecium growing on agar. B, apex of ripe ascus (in optical section) showing ascus wall and three spores, but omitting protoplasmic contents and ascospore sheaths. C, single spore with mucilage sheath.

the sporangiophore of *Pilobolus*, the individual projecting asci of *Dasyobolus* and the phototropic sporophore of *Sphaerobolus* (Fig. 28). However, it is necessary to bear in mind that phototropism in relation to spore discharge is not entirely limited to coprophilous species.

The mature ascus is a single highly-turgid cell bounded by a thin cell-wall. At its tip is a minute depression and at the base

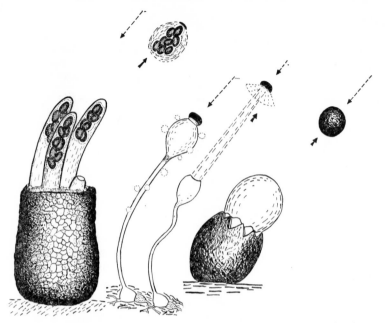

Fig. 28. Diagram of phototropism in relation to spore discharge in, from left to right, *Dasyobolus immersus* (×40), *Pilobolus kleinii* (×10), and *Sphaerobolus stellatus* (×10). Long arrows show direction of light and short arrows the direction in which projectiles are moving. The drawing of discharge in *Pilobolus*, showing the almost cylindrical sap-jet and the skirt of spray around the sporangium, is based on Page (1964).

of this the cell-wall is especially thin. This becomes the apical pore through which the spores escape when the ascus eventually bursts (Fig. 27). Lining the ascus wall is a thin layer of enucleate protoplasm. The eight ascospores are contained in the apical region of the large sap-vacuole which forms the greater part of the ascus. The black ascospores form a single line. Each is about 22 × 13 μ, although the actual size depends on the particular isolate and the conditions of culture. The spore is surrounded by a conspicuous sheath of mucilage about 3 μ wide.

In *Sordaria* a ripe ascus, whilst still remaining attached to a basal cushion within the perithecium, elongates up the neck canal, which can accommodate only one at a time, until its tip projects beyond the ostiole. It then ruptures squirting its contents into the air, its envelope retracting into the perithecium where it rapidly gelatinizes.

The pore through which escape occurs is only 4 μ across whilst the rigid spore has a diameter of about 13 μ. The pore must, therefore, be considerably stretched during discharge. Contraction will tend to occur after each spore escapes and before the pore begins to be stretched again by the next one in the row. Because of their mucilaginous sheaths, successive spores tend to stick together, but the contracting pore may break this connexion and this no doubt explains the fact that, in a spore deposit formed from perithecia discharging horizontally, spores occur singly and also in groups of two to eight.

This matter was investigated experimentally (Ingold and Hadland, 1959) using cultures on filter-paper-yeast-extract agar poured brimfull into specimen tubes 2·5 × 2·5 cm and grown with overhead lighting so that the perithecial necks were parallel to the longitudinal axis of the culture tube. A culture of this kind was then placed on its side in a long black box (Fig. 29) and illuminated with a horizontal beam of light. Spores discharged horizontally fell onto a graduated glass slide in the box. After a suitable period the slide was examined microscopically and the number (1–8) of spores in each sporegroup and its distance of discharge were recorded. The results of a typical experiment are shown in Fig. 30. It is to be observed that the largest number of projectiles were 1-spored; thereafter the number of projectiles of increasing size fell to the 7-spored type, but rose again for the 8-spored type. It can be shown that this is what is often to be expected if the chance of a break occurring in the chain of eight escaping spores is equal at each of the seven links in the chain.

The tendency for spores to separate (θ) can be calculated from the expression:

$$\theta = \frac{N - \frac{1}{8}n}{\frac{7}{8}n},$$

where N is the total number of groups of spores, n the total

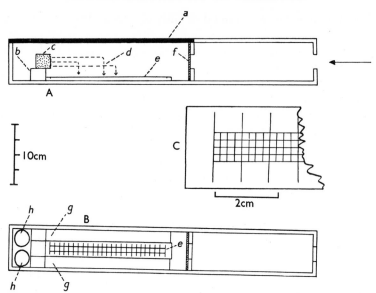

FIG. 29. Wooden box used in studying horizontal distance of spore discharge in *Sordaria*. A, vertical section of box: *a*, removable lid; *b*, culture holder. C, specimen-tube culture of fungus; *d*, trajectories of discharged spores; *e*, graduated slide; *f*, glass window. The arrow shows the direction of the incident light. B, plan view of box: *e*, graduated slide; *g*, wooden guides holding slide in position; *h*, specimen tubes containing water. C, small part of graduated slide, at a larger scale, to show details of ruling.

number of spores, and therefore the number of links between spores is $\frac{7}{8}n$. If the spores always separate from one another (i.e., N equals n) then the value of θ is 1·0; if the spores always stick together (i.e., each group consists always of 8 spores), θ is zero.

In the experiment illustrated in Fig. 30 the value of θ is 0·168. It has been remarked that the number of 8-spored groups considerably exceeds that of 7-spored groups. It can be shown mathematically that the number decreases from 1-spored to 7-spored groups and then rises or continues to fall so far as the 8-spore group is concerned according as θ is less than or exceeds 0·3. Figure 31 shows the actual number of groups of each size, and also the theoretical curve based on the

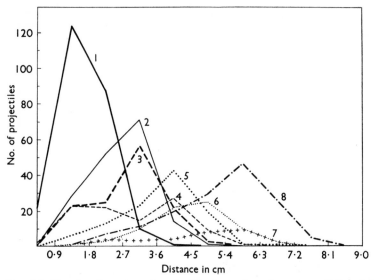

FIG. 30. Graphs of number of projectiles (in each major square (0·9 × 0·9 cm) of graduated slide (see Fig. 29)) plotted against distance from culture for each of the eight sizes of projectile. The figure associated with each graph indicates the number of spores per projectile. This is Experiment 1 (see Fig. 31).

view that a break is equally likely between any two escaping spores. The agreement between observation and this theory is clearly good.

No doubt the tendency for spores to stick together is affected by the viscosity of the mucilage around the spore. Since increase in temperature lowers viscosity, it might be reasonable to suppose that the θ value would increase with temperature. This has proved to be so. In one experiment the value of θ at 21–24°C was 0·252 and at 7–10°C, 0·183; in another θ had a value of 0·288 at the higher and 0·227 at the lower temperature (Ingold and Hadland, 1959).

A consideration of the distribution by size of the spore-groups in a deposit formed by the settling of spores discharged horizontally leads to information about the behaviour of the ascus jet during discharge. Another and more direct approach to

57

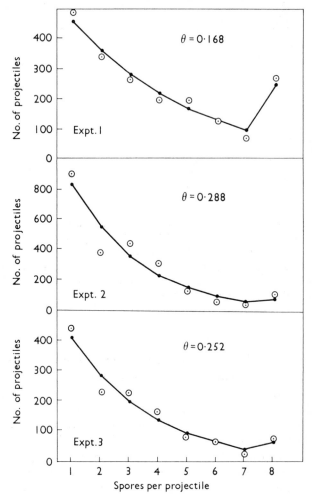

F ɪ ɢ. 31. Number of projectiles plotted against number of spores per projectile (Expt. 1 is the same as that referred to in Fig. 30.) The solid line connects the theoretical values calculated from the given value of θ and the total number of spores involved.

the problem involves catching the jets on the unde.
'perspex' disk rotating very rapidly in a horizontal plane
above discharging perithecia (Fig. 32). The elements of individual jets, if the speed of rotation is sufficient, become
spread out horizontally on the disk and can be observed

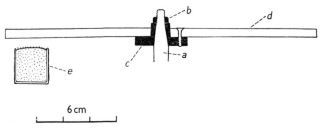

6 cm

FIG. 32. Sectional view of apparatus used to study the form of ascus jets:
a, spindle of electric motor; *b*, nut; *c*, brass socket made to fit spindle; *d*,
perspex disk; *e*, fruiting culture of *Sordaria*.

microscopically. A number of such impaled jets of *Sordaria
fimicola* are illustrated in Fig. 33. It can be seen that in an ascus
jet there are not only spores in groups of various sizes and ascus
sap associated with them, but also isolated droplets of sap.
Further it is clear that if the rate of rotation of the surface of the
disk directly above the discharging culture is known, the time
taken for the escape of the jet from the ascus can be estimated.
It works out at about 0·00005 seconds.

It has generally been supposed that in some Ascomycetes the
spores of an ascus separate from one another on discharge,
whilst in others they always stick together. Further it has been
suggested that the gluing together of spores to form a single
projectile is especially a feature of coprophilous fungi. This may
indeed be roughly true, but probably all types exist between
species where the spores always stick together, as in *Saccobolus*
spp. and in *Dasyobolus immersus*, and those in which they
always separate. Further the tendency for spores to stick
together is not limited to coprophilous fungi. For example, in
the lignicolous *Daldinia concentrica*, as in *Sordaria*, all types of
projectiles from 1-spored to 8-spored are formed with, however,

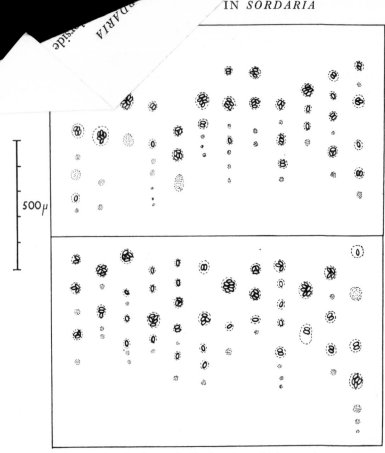

FIG. 33. *Sordaria fimicola.* *Camera lucida* drawings of 24 ascus jets caught on the under surface of a rotating 'perspex' disk. In all the front end of the jet is uppermost. The rate of movement of the part of the disk above the discharging perithecia was 1672 cm/sec.

quite a strong tendency for the spores to separate from one another ($\theta = 0\cdot40$).

In *Sordaria fimicola* spores are discharged horizontally up to a distance of about 10 cm and it can be shown that, for the size of projectile involved, the maximum vertical throw is only slightly less. The larger projectiles are shot on the average to

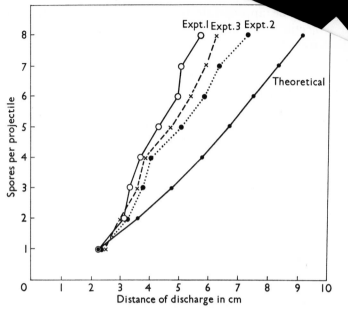

FIG. 34. Average distance of discharge for each of the eight sizes of projectile plotted against number of spores per projectile. Results from three separate experiments. The theoretical curve is based on $D = Kr^2$ (see p. 4) with the value of K selected to give the observed distance for single spores in Experiment 1 (see Fig. 30).

a greater distance than the smaller ones. We have already seen that with a given muzzle velocity the distance (D) to which a spherical projectile is discharged can be expressed by: $D = Kr^2$ (see p. 4). Thus assuming that all *Sordaria* projectiles irrespective of number of spores have the same take-off velocity and that they are spherical, we should expect the larger ones to carry further. However, the average distances actually observed for spore groups of increasing size are less than expected (Fig. 34). This may well be due to the fact that these projectiles probably depart considerably from the spherical form in the earlier stages of their flight. Thus an 8-spored projectile presumably starts as an elongated jet which only later rounds off under the influence of surface tension as it rapidly loses velocity.

...mphasize here the importance
...r factor in determining distance of
...rizontal throw by a series of sordari-
...*ldinia*, only projectiles consisting of the
...nt were considered (Ingold, 1961). The
...in *Podospora taenioides*, but 8-spored in all the
rest. It will be seen (Table I) that the average distance increased steadily with increasing projectile size.

TABLE I

Projectile size and horizontal distance of spore discharge (all projectiles 8-spored except for *Podospora taenioides* in which they are 4-spored)

Species	Average dimensions of ascospore (μ)	Calculated total volume of spore complement in ascus (μ^3)	Average distance (cm) of discharge of full ascus complement
Daldinia concentrica	14·2 × 6·8	2626	0·9
Sordaria fimicola (A)	17·3 × 11·0	8325	3·2
S. fimicola (B)	21·5 × 13·1	14465	6·4
Podospora minuta	21·0 × 14·8	18413	10·6
Ascobolus leveillei	28·8 × 15·6	28016	11·5
Sordaria fimicola (C)†	32·1 × 16·3	34432	12·0
Podospora taenioides	46·0 × 24·0	52992	32·3

† Three isolates of *S. fimicola* have been used (A, B, and C). Many would put isolate C in *Sordaria macrospora*.

Having reviewed the structure of *Sordaria* and the general problem of its ballistics, we may pass on to consider how spore discharge is influenced by external factors. These are: (1) the water-supply to the perithecium, (2) temperature, (3) light, and (4) the composition of the surrounding air particularly in relation to its humidity and carbon dioxide content.

For all Ascomycetes and Basidiomycetes which discharge their spores violently, water supply is of major importance and this matter will be treated more fully in a later chapter. Here it need only be emphasized that in *Sordaria* also this factor is paramount. In the experimental work carried out on spore discharge in *Sordaria*, the fungus has been grown on nutrient agar. Since under these circumstances the basal part of the perithecium is immersed in a soft aqueous jelly, water supply is probably never limiting.

It seems that under natural conditions of temperature and illumination spore discharge in *Sordaria fimicola* is periodic with a day-time maximum, and this rhythm appears to be related primarily to light. Nevertheless, light is not necessary for perithecium production and spore discharge. Cultures grown in continuous darkness fruit apparently as freely as controls in light and, further, they discharge their spores. This is not true, however, for all sordariaceous fungi. Thus an isolate of *Podospora setosa* was found to require light for perithecium development, although a mutant strain derived from this produced perithecia equally well in dark as in light.

Before discussing the stimulatory effect of illumination, it may be well to make brief reference to the methods that have been used in following changes in the rate of spore discharge. Usually cultures have been grown in $2 \cdot 5 \times 2 \cdot 5$ cm specimen tubes filled with filter-paper-yeast-extract agar. For short-period experiments a small black 'perspex' box to contain the culture has been employed. This can be illuminated by a small window in the lid and a lateral drawer serves as a holder which, when in position, exposes a glass slide, with a convenient grid etched on its under surface, just above the discharging perithecia (Ingold and Dring, 1957). By counting the spores shot onto this in a given time the rate of spore liberation can be determined. For experiments of longer duration either a 'spore-train' (Ingold and Dring 1957) or a 'spore-clock' has been used. The spore-clock is, perhaps, the more satisfactory piece of apparatus (Ingold and Marshall, 1963) and is illustrated in Fig. 35. A very shallow box of black 'perspex', with a cubicle below to accommodate the discharging culture, has rotating horizontally in it a disk of transparent 'perspex'. This, attached to the vertical axis of a clockwork mechanism, completes a single rotation in just over twenty-four hours. Spores are discharged onto the under surface of the disk which has a suitable grid etched on it. In the lid of the box above the cubicle is a small window through which the fungus can be illuminated. If, however, this is blacked-out the interior is in darkness. The whole lid of the box is detachable but when in position it can be secured by screws at the corners, a tight fit being assured by having a rubber washer, in the form of a square frame, between the lid and the walls of the box. Entry and exit tubes near the top of the cubicle allow an air stream to

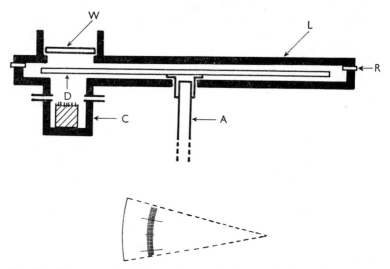

Fig. 35. Above: sectional view of spore-clock; one third actual size. Black 'perspex' indicated by very thick black lines. L, lid of box; R, rubber washer; W, light filter; C, cubicle containing culture and fitted with inlet and outlet tubes; D, rotating transparent 'perspex' disk; A, vertical rotating axis connected to clock (not shown). Below: a sector of the 'perspex' disk seen in surface view showing graduations.

be passed over the culture if desired. At the end of a day the disk can be removed and hourly rates of discharge determined by suitable counts under the microscope.

When a culture of *Sordaria fimicola* is subjected to a daily régime involving 12 hours' light and 12 hours of darkness, with all other conditions kept constant, discharge is mainly during the light periods. After transfer to light from darkness discharge rises to a high level several hours later and then declines. However, it takes some considerable time to reach a steady level in the light, a 12-hour period being insufficient (Fig. 36, A). Nevertheless, whether a steady level has been attained or not, transfer to darkness invariably leads to a decline in the rate of discharge. The height of the peak in the rate of spore

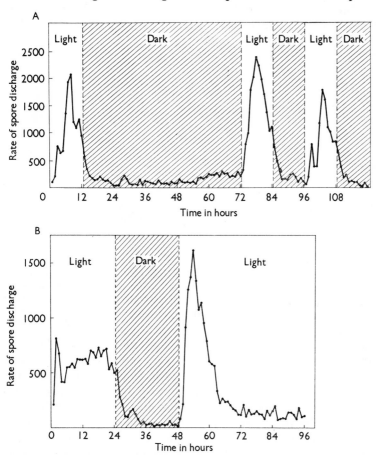

FIG. 36. *Sordaria fimicola.*

A, rate of spore discharge plotted against time for a culture which has, previous to the start of the experiment, been grown with 12 hours' light and 12 hours' dark in each 24-hour period.

B, similar type of graph for a culture grown in continuous light and then treated as shown in figure.

liberation which occurs some hours after transfer from dark to light is conditioned, to a considerable extent, by the duration of the preceding dark period (Fig. 36, C).

In these experiments there is no indication of an endogenous rhythm in *Sordaria fimicola*, such as occurs in the nocturnal *Daldinia*, even in a culture which has been raised from the start under a 12 hours' light : 12 hours' dark regimen (Fig. 36, A).

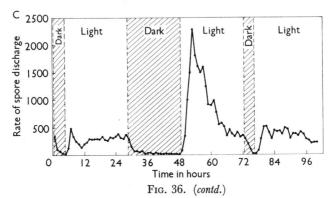

FIG. 36. (*contd.*)

C, similar type of graph for culture grown in continuous light up to the start of the experiment and then treated as shown in figure. Periods of darkness stippled. Temp. 21°C. Light from 'daylight' fluorescent tubes approximately 1000 lux. After Ingold and Dring (1957).

Since transfer to light has such a profound effect on the rate of spore discharge especially following a sufficient period in the dark, it is natural to consider how far very short periods of illumination may trigger-off the process. In a series of experiments involving rather high light intensities (about 10000 lux) operating for 10 minutes or less, it was found that 2–3 hours after treatment the rate of discharge rose to a level of the order of ten times the original one, followed by a rapid decline (Fig. 37).

In the stimulation of spore discharge by light in *Sordaria* it is the blue end of the visible spectrum that is active, light above 520 mμ being ineffective (Ingold, 1958). It is further of interest to note that there are two other and very different processes affected by light: the phototropism of the perithecial necks and the production of a red carotenoid pigment. All three processes appear to have essentially the same action spectrum.

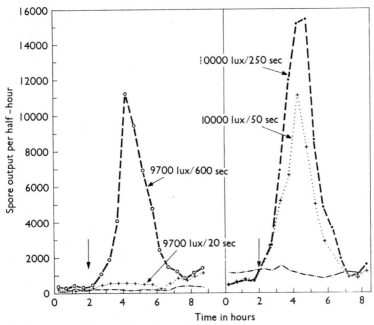

FIG. 37. *Sordaria fimicola*. Two sets of curves showing rate of spore discharge (in spores caught on 1 cm² surface above a discharging culture per ½ hour) plotted against time. Prior to zero time cultures in dark for about 20 hours. Indicated short light treatment given at time shown by vertical arrow. In each set of curves there is an untreated control.

The chemical nature of the photoreceptor remains unknown. When the perithecia together with the mycelium are treated with such organic solvents as ethanol or acetone, an orange extract is obtained. Analysis by paper chromatography indicates that the colour is due to the presence of both a red and a yellow pigment. The red one is clearly a carotenoid absorbing visible light mainly between 400 and 520 mμ with peaks (in petrol ether) at 445, 472, and 505 mμ, thus agreeing closely with lycopene. The nature of the yellow pigment is unknown. It shows a rising absorption on passing from 500 mμ to 400 mμ. The red pigment is produced only in the light whilst the yellow one is formed equally freely in darkness.

The current view (Ingold, 1962) is that the photoreceptor in light-dependent processes in fungi is either a carotene, or a flavin such as riboflavin, possibly in association with a protein. At present evidence tends to favour the flavin theory.

A number of other sordariaceous fungi exhibit light-stimulated discharge of their ascospores. It is, for example, a feature of *Podospora curvula* and *P. setosa*. However, in some Pyrenomycetes light has the opposite effect and markedly inhibits discharge. This is particularly true of *Hypoxylon fuscum* (Ingold and Marshall, 1963).

The rate of spore discharge in *Sordaria* is, naturally, affected by temperature, but the effect of a particular temperature is conditioned by previous treatment. Thus in the dark transfer after 24 hours at 20 to 25°C leads to a great increase in rate of discharge after a few hours, but then the rate falls rapidly and at the end of 24 hours at the higher temperature is not very different from the rate at 20°C. Further a return to 20°C for the following day produces little alteration in rate, but when the culture is again subjected to 24 hours at the higher temperature the characteristic peak is repeated (Fig. 38, A).

When the same régime is employed but with alternating days of light (c. 1000 lux) and darkness in which the illuminated days are either during the period of high (Fig. 38, C) or low (Fig. 38, B) temperature, it is found that spore discharge is at an enormously higher rate during the light days as compared with the dark ones irrespective of temperature. The familiar peak several hours after transfer to light is clearly shown. Essentially the same result is obtained when the contrasted temperatures are 15 and 25°C.

In continuous darkness with a régime involving days at 8°C alternating others at 20°C, discharge falls quickly to nearly zero at the lower temperature and rises at the higher to a peak 8–10 hours after transfer and thereafter rapidly declines (Fig. 39). In a parallel experiment with the cold periods

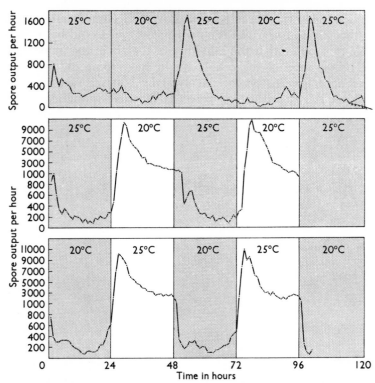

Fig. 38. *Sordaria fimicola*. Upper curve: rate of spore discharge from culture grown in the dark at 20°C and then subjected to alternate days at 25°C and 20°C in dark. Lower two curves: two parallel experiments on cultures reared in light at 20°C and then treated as shown with alternating days at 20°C and 25°C and alternating days of darkness and light (1000 lux, 'daylight' fluorescent); in one relatively high temperature and darkness coincide; in the other relatively high temperature and light.

illuminated the picture is the same (Fig. 39). Light appears to have no effect in stimulating discharge at 8°C. It thus seems that at higher temperatures light is limiting whilst under colder conditions temperature becomes the limiting factor.

In nature there is a marked diurnal periodicity in discharge with a daytime peak. In the production of this temperature and light no doubt co-operate, but probably, at least in spring and summer, light is the master factor.

69

Since only the lower part of the perithecium is submerged in the substratum whilst the neck projects, it would be reasonable to suppose that the humidity of the air in the immediate neighbourhood of the ostiole might have some influence on discharge. As this process involves the bursting of turgescent cells, it might further be expected that low humidity would

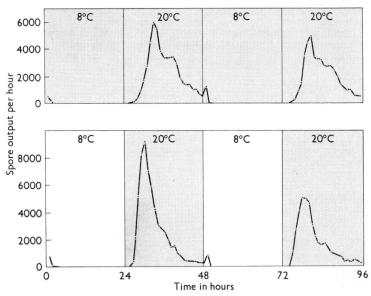

FIG. 39. *Sordaria fimicola*. Upper curve: culture reared in light at 20°C and then subjected in darkness to alternating days at 8°C and 20°C. Lower curve: parallel culture but illuminated (1000 lux 'daylight' fluorescent) during the cold periods.

militate against discharge. However, experiments indicate that low humidity, provided it does not persist too long, greatly stimulates discharge. In an experiment, the results of which are illustrated in Fig. 40, for alternating hours a saturated air-stream and a very dry one (approximately R.H. 35 per cent) were circulated over a culture. The rate of discharge was much higher in the dry as compared with the humid periods. However, with more prolonged dry periods the rate of discharge, though initially high, steadily fell and in a following damp period, although discharge rate was originally low, it steadily rose (Ingold and Marshall, 1962).

It is not clear how general this positive response to low humidity may be in Pyrenomycetes and the subject is in need of critical examination.

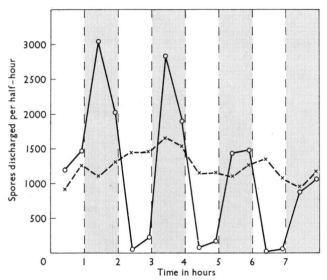

FIG. 40. Rate of spore discharge from illuminated cultures of *Sordaria* plotted against time. Dotted line: control culture in water-saturated air-streams. Continuous line: culture alternately in damp air-stream (un-stippled periods) and in dry (entering stream 35% R.H.) air-stream (stippled period). Both cultures before start of experiment subjected to damp air-stream for 15 hours.

Another constituent of air which might have an influence on the rate of discharge is carbon dioxide. Experiments show that even as low a concentration as 0·2 per cent considerably stimulates discharge as compared with carbon-dioxide-free air (Fig. 41). However, the amount usually present in the atmosphere (0·03 per cent) is without effect. Normal air deprived of its carbon dioxide, and untreated air have indistinguishable effects on spore liberation in *Sordaria*. Only rarely can the carbon dioxide in the air build up locally to as high a level as

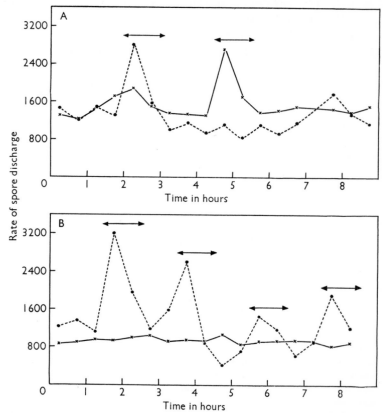

Fig. 41. *Sordaria fimicola*. Two experiments on rate of spore discharge (as number of spores caught on 1 cm² slide surface above a culture in half an hour) plotted against time. Temperature 20°C, light intensity 700 lux, rate of air-flow 250 ml/min. Hourly periods when air with 0·2 per cent CO_2 was passing over culture indicated by horizontal lines with arrowheads; otherwise air-streams consisted of laboratory air minus CO_2 in A and cylinder air minus CO_2 in B. A. Interrupted line: CO_2 at 2–3 hrs from start. Solid line: CO_2 at $4\frac{1}{2}$–$5\frac{1}{2}$ hrs, from start. B. Solid line: CO_2-free air throughout. Interrupted line: CO_2 from $1\frac{1}{2}$–$2\frac{1}{2}$ hrs, $3\frac{1}{2}$–$4\frac{1}{2}$ hrs, $5\frac{1}{2}$–$6\frac{1}{2}$ hrs, and $7\frac{1}{2}$–$8\frac{1}{2}$ hrs.

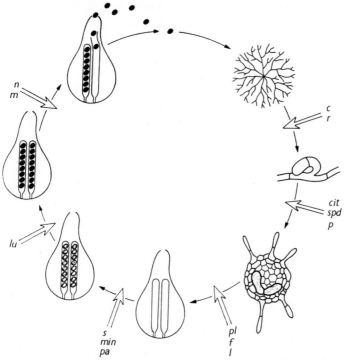

Fig. 42. *Sordaria macrospora.* Diagram showing the position of genetic blocks in perithecium development. The lettering indicates specific genes which, when present as recessive alleles, block further development at the indicated positions in the process of perithecium and ascus formation. From Esser and Straub (1958).

0·2 per cent and it is, therefore, unlikely that variations in this factor have any effect on discharge in nature.

We are, therefore, left with a still very incomplete picture of spore discharge in *Sordaria fimicola* as an active process influenced by a range of external factors. But it is not at all clear at what stage or stages in the development of an ascus a particular factor exerts its effect. Temperature would presumably affect all the enzyme-controlled processes involved in ascus matur-ation, whereas light might, perhaps, influence only one particular chemical reaction. Probably the effect of humidity is physical rather than chemical, but it is difficult to envisage the mode of action of reduced humidity as a stimulant to discharge.

Finally it should be noted that there are internal as well as external factors which may influence discharge. Esser and Straub (1958) have made a very extensive study of mutant blocks in the perithecium development of *Sordaria macrospora* (Fig. 42). Each mutation prevented further development beyond a certain point. One stopped the final stage of spore discharge. Accepting the concept of 'one gene, one enzyme', it would seem that some enzyme-controlled reaction is involved in the final preparation for the bursting of the ascus. It would be of great interest to know the nature of this. Possibly it involves the hydrolysis of a polysaccharide to a sugar in the final build-up of osmotic pressure in the ascus.

REFERENCES

BULLER, A. H. R. (1933). *Researches on Fungi* Vol. V. London.

CALLAGHAN, A. A. (1961). Studies on sordariaceous fungi. Unpublished M.Sc. Thesis, University of London.

ESSER, K. and STRAUB, J. (1958). Genetische Untersuchungen an *Sordaria macrospora* Auersw., Kompensation und Induktion bei genbedingten Entwicklungsdefeckten. *Z. Verebungslehre* **80,** 729–746.

INGOLD, C. T. (1958). On light-stimulated spore discharge in *Sordaria*. *Ann. Bot.* **22,** 129–135.

—— (1961). Ballistics in certain Ascomyetes. *New Phyt.* **60,** 143–149.

—— (1962). The reaction of fungi to light and the problem of photo-reception. In *Biological receptor mechanisms S.E.B. Symposium* **16,** 154–169. Cambridge.

INGOLD, C. T. and DRING, V. J. (1957). An analysis of spore discharge in *Sordaria*. *Ann. Bot.* **21,** 465–477.

INGOLD, C. T. and HADLAND, S. A. (1959). The ballistics of *Sordaria*. *New Phyt.* **58,** 46–57.

INGOLD, C. T. and MARSHALL, B. (1962). Stimulation of spore discharge by reduced humidity in *Sordaria*. *Ann. Bot.* **26,** 563–568.

—— (1963). Further observations on light and spore discharge in certain Pyrenomycetes. *Ann. Bot.* **27,** 481–491.

—— (1964). Stimulation of spore discharge in *Sordaria* by carbon dioxide. *Ann. Bot.* **28,** 325–329.

PAGE, R. M. (1964). Sporangium discharge in *Pilobolus:* a photographic study. *Science* **146,** 925–927.

IV

THE WATER-RELATIONS OF
SPORE LIBERATION IN
TERRESTRIAL FUNGI

THE discharge of ascospores in most Ascomycetes by ascus bursting, and of basidiospores by the drop-excretion mechanism found in the majority of Basidiomycetes, seems to involve the activity of turgid cells. Again where a rounding-off mechanism occurs as in aecidiospore discharge in rusts, the liberation of conidia in species of *Entomophthora* and *Conidiobolus*, or the catapulting of the glebal-mass in *Sphaerobolus*, turgidity of the cells is essential. Generally speaking, therefore, spore liberation in fungi necessitates a supply of water to the active regions in order to maintain turgidity. This is in contrast to archegoniate cryptogams in which dry conditions involving water loss are almost invariably concerned with spore liberation. Nevertheless, there are certain fungi in which evaporation is the normal prelude to violent spore release. Thus the hygroscopic twirling of conidiophores on drying leads to discharge in *Peronospora tabacina*, and probably in a number of similar fungi, and the separation of a gas phase in structures distorted by evaporation is responsible for discharge in some dematiaceous Hyphomycetes. Again in a number of fungi, including conidial fungi, some Gasteromycetes and most Mycetozoa, although the spores may not be violently discharged, dry conditions favour their take-off.

We may first consider the water-relations of Ascomycetes. A number of fleshy species belonging to such genera as *Peziza*, *Leotia*, *Helvella*, and *Morchella* have little power of withstanding drought and, like most agarics, can function only under sufficiently humid conditions. However, the great majority of Ascomycetes, and particularly most Pyrenomycetes, are drought-enduring xerophytes. These discharge their spores only when wet. During dry periods they lose water becoming temporarily

75

inactive, but rapidly recover and discharge spores on wetting. Few precise observations seem to have been made of the ability of these fungi to survive long periods of dryness. However, the author has kept stromata of *Hypoxylon fuscum* in a refrigerator in tubes with anhydrous calcium chloride, and subsequently tested their activity. After eighteen months perithecia could still discharge spores within a day or two of stromata being placed on wet filter paper. In nature, however, where repeated

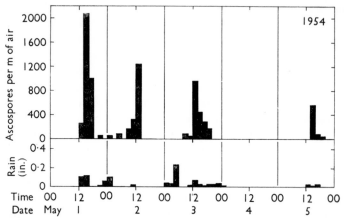

FIG. 43. *Venturia inaequalis*. Relation between rainfall and concentration of ascospores per cubic metre of air in an apple orchard every two hours during the first five days of May. After Hirst *et. al.* (1955).

wetting and drying occur and where extremes of temperature are encountered, such a fungus as *H. fuscum* probably remains active for only a single season of not more than six months' duration.

The relationship of discharge to wetting by rain has been shown very clearly in an epidemiological study of the apple scab fungus, *Venturia inaequalis*, in an orchard and also in laboratory experiments (Hirst *et al.*, 1955; Hirst and Stedman, 1962). The perithecia develop on dead leaves on the ground. During the late spring, when maturation occurs, there is a close correlation between periods of rainfall and of high ascospore-content of the orchard air as measured by a Hirst spore trap (Fig. 43). Dew has little effect in bringing about spore discharge, but a light rainfall of only 0·2 mm leads to abundant release of ascospores. Following rain the majority of the spores are set free in the first three hours.

In *Ophiobolus graminis* (Gregory and Stedman, 1958) spores are discharged shortly after a wetting, provided this is equal to at least 0·25 mm of rain, and the rate of release rises to a maximum within the hour. It then fairly rapidly declines to zero and thereafter discharge will not recommence until the material

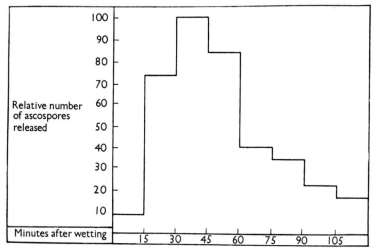

FIG. 44 *Ophiobolus graminis*. Rate of release of ascospores (spores trapped per 15 min as percentage of peak rate) in wind tunnel, plotted against time. After Gregory and Stedman (1958).

is dried before rewetting (Fig. 44). Probably this type of behaviour is fairly widespread.

Although it must be emphasized that the drought-enduring type of xerophyte is the rule in Ascomycetes, there are a few unusual examples in which discharge can be sustained, for a time at least, under dry conditions without the necessity for direct wetting with rain. A notable example is *Daldinia concentrica* (Fig. 45) which produces its large hemispherical perithecial stromata, often the size of half an apple, on ash (*Fraxinus*), and also on other trees, especially birch (*Betula*) and gorse (*Ulex*), if these have been scorched by fire. The stromata mature in late April or May and continue to shed their spores at night-time throughout the summer. If in mid-April a stroma is detached, brought indoors, and placed in a relatively dry atmosphere without any extraneous supply of water, spore discharge may continue for three of four weeks. During this time the stroma with its firm rigid crust undergoes no appreciable change of volume, but its density declines from just over

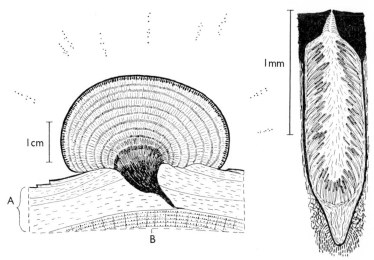

Fig. 45. *Daldinia concentrica*. Left, perithecial stroma on ash branch in sectional view with some discharged spores in the air. The black dots just within the outer crust (indicated by the thick black line) are perithecia: A, bark; B, wood. Right, a single perithecium.

1·0 to, perhaps, 0·3. Clearly during this period the water necessary for spore discharge has been obtained from a reserve in the stromatal tissue. Even if a stroma is placed in a desiccator over anhydrous calcium chloride, spore discharge continues for many days (Ingold, 1946 and 1960).

It is by no means clear how water is transferred from the stromatal tissue to the perithecia, but sections show a three-dimensional network of veins which may be involved in translocation.

TABLE II

Daldinia. Spore discharge

Observations started	Start of discharge	End of discharge	Period of discharge (days)
I. *Detached stroma in laboratory*			
7 April	17 April	17 May	30
10 April	27 April	23 May	26
II. *Stroma on tree trunk*			
9 March	3 May	17 Sept.	138

A stroma attached to a tree seems to remain active much longer than a detached one. In Table II records are given of two isolated stromata which were brought indoors in early April. In these once discharge started it continued for about a month. Spore output was also followed from a stroma attached to an ash-tree. The set-up is shown in Fig. 46. Just above the

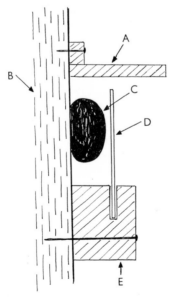

Fig. 46. *Daldinia concentrica.* Set-up used in study of spore discharge from a stroma on a standing tree: A, roof, B, ash trunk; C, stroma; D, glass slide; E, slide-holder.

79

stroma was a small wooden roof, as a protection from rain, and arranged below was a slide-holder in which a vertical glass-slide could be placed to catch the discharged spores. This slide was changed daily from early March to late September. Discharge started on 3 May and continued nightly until 17 September, a period of 138 days (see Table II). This longer period of discharge from an attached specimen may well be associated with the gradual replenishment of the water reserve in the stroma from the tree trunk.

It is worth noticing that *Daldinia* is a fungus with a summer discharge period and this is possible because of its curious water-relations. Most other lignicolous Pyrenomycetes discharge their spores in autumn when conditions are more humid.

Another summer fungus with unusual water-relations is *Epichloe typhina*, causing 'choke' of grasses (Ingold, 1948). Aerial shoots of infected grasses such as *Dactylis*, *Holcus*, *Brachypodium*, and *Agrostis* fail to flower. Instead, just above a node, a fungal stroma is produced. At an early stage this is whitish and produces abundant conidia, but in late July or August it turns orange-yellow becoming studded with closely-set perithecia. At this stage a transverse section of the affected region shows the fungal tissue intimately associated with the folded living grass leaves (Fig. 47). If a grass stalk attacked by 'choke' is cut with a razor (making the cut under water and thereafter keeping the cut end submerged) and brought into the laboratory, the course of spore liberation can be followed using the set-up illustrated in Fig. 47. The actual rate of spore output can be determined by placing a slide in a fixed position below the stroma and counting the spores deposited on a defined area in a given time. The rate is not constant; there tends to be a day-time minimum and a night-time maximum. If in the evening, when the rate of spore liberation is high and rising, the stalk of the grass is severed above its water supply, spore discharge falls to zero usually within the hour. Apparently the fungus derives the necessary water for discharge from the transpiration stream of its host, and is not dependent directly on wetting by rain.

Another example of an ascomycete in which spore discharge

can continue in a dry atmosphere for some time without a sustained external supply of water is *Bulgaria inquinans*. The relatively large black apothecia, common on dead limbs and trunks of beech and oak in autumn, are somewhat like lumps of black india-rubber. The bulk of the thick apothecium, which may be 2–3 cm across and weigh as much as 10 g, consists of aqueous jelly representing a modification of the outer layers of the hyphal walls (Fig. 48). If a thick median slice of an apothecium is laid horizontally on a glass plate, a black spore deposit is formed extending to about 2 mm from the edge of the hymenium. The colour is due to black spores, but there are colourless ones as well. This species is remarkable in having, within each ascus, four nearly black and four smaller unpigmented spores. If a detached apothecium is hung upside down by a thread from a horizontal glass rod supported on the rim of a beaker, the spores deposited inside the beaker can be collected and counted at intervals. The gradual loss of water from the apothecium can at the same time be followed by weighing it at intervals. It is found that in a dry atmosphere spore discharge can go on for several days, though at a declining rate. It ultimately ceases only when the apothecium is reduced to less than a quarter of its original weight. The actual picture of fall in the rate of spore release with decrease in weight is complicated by a diurnal rhythm in a specimen subjected to normal alternation of day and night (Fig. 48). Unlike the gelatinous Basidiomycetes, a dried and subsequently resoaked specimen of *Bulgaria* has little capacity for further spore discharge (Ingold, 1959).

Sustained spore discharge under dry conditions over a period of several days without any outside supply of water is possible because of the available water stored in the jelly of the apothecium. It may, perhaps, be reasonable to suggest that wherever a relatively large amount of jelly is to be found in a fungal structure, it represents an immediately available water reserve.

Another example of this principle is to be found in the stink-horn, *Phallus impudicus* (see p. 156). This is a fungus of summer and early autumn, which gradually stores water in

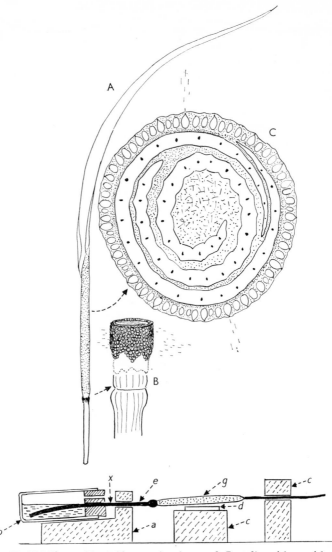

FIG. 47. *Epichloe typhina.* Above: A, shoot of *Dactylis* with perithecial stroma above node; B, details of region above node; C, transverse section showing stroma with perithecia. Fungal tissue is dotted; leaves white with vascular bundles as black dots. In B and C discharged spores are seen in the air around the stroma. Below: method of measuring rate of spore discharge: *a*, cork support; *b*, specimen tube containing water; *c*, wooden block; *d*, glass slide; *e*, stem of grass; *g*, stroma of fungus; *x*, point at which stem can be cut to stop transpiration stream.

82

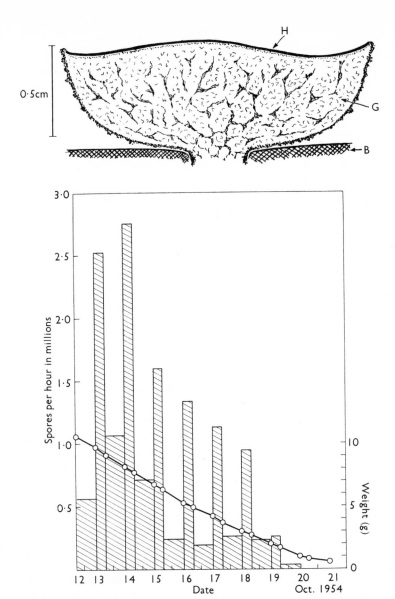

Fig. 48. *Bulgaria inquinans*. Above: vertical section through apothecium.
H, hymenium; G, mass of gelatinous tissue permeated by a system of
anastomosing veins; B, bark. Below: diagram of spore liberation from a
single drying apothecium. The continuous line refers to weight plotted
against time. The histogram shows average hourly rate of spore liberation
for day periods (10 a.m.–6 p.m.) and for night periods (6 p.m.–10 a.m.).

the subterranean 'egg', mainly in the jelly of the middle peridium. When ripe the stipe within the 'egg' rapidly elongates carrying the cap with its stinking spore-slime above the substratum. The growth of the stipe, which happens with remarkable speed, requires a considerable supply of water which seems to come from the jelly.

Apart from the general question of the necessity for a steady supply of water to the hymenium if spore discharge is to continue in an ascomycete, there is the problem of the direct effect of atmospheric humidity. There is evidence that, at least in some species, very high humidity may retard discharge. This has already been considered in *Sordaria fimicola* in which short periods of low humidity have been shown to stimulate spore discharge (see p. 70). Again low humidity may encourage discharge in some Discomycetes. The 'puffing' of larger cup-fungi which occurs so often after a period of quiescence, may be induced by a sudden decrease in the humidity of the air in contact with the hymenium. In experiments on *Ascophanus carneus*, similar to those reported in *Sordaria*, a period of low humidity, if not too long, is found to increase the rate of spore liberation.

We may now turn our attention to the huge group of Hymenomycetes and to the gelatinous Heterobasidiomycetes in all of which spore discharge occurs. The spores of the basidium are normally liberated in succession and it is only after the last one has been shot away that the basidium slowly collapses. Whatever may be the exact mechanism of discharge (see Chapter VI), it seems that the system can work only if the basidia retain their turgidity.

In those Basidiomycetes which actively shed their spores, as with Ascomycetes but more so, there are many species without any powers of resistance to drought. Most of the fleshy agarics are of this kind and their short-lived sporophores tend to be produced in autumn when the humidity of the air near the ground is high, and before the frosts of winter put a limit to their existence. But, as in Ascomycetes, there are many drought-enduring xerophytes which dry and cease to discharge their spores under conditions of drought. However, they remain alive, rapidly absorb water on being wetted by rain and very soon afterwards begin to liberate spores again. To this group belong most of the corky and leathery polypores and other bracket fungi so common on wood, and also the gelatinous fungi such as *Auricularia, Tremella,* and *Calocera.*

Buller (1909) has drawn particular attention to *Schizophyllum commune* (Fig. 49). This is a small gill-bearing bracket fungus found the world over and common in southern England on the dead trunks and branches of beech *(Fagus)*. A curious feature of the genus is that the gills are split lengthwise. When the weather is damp and spore discharge is taking place, the gills look quite normal, but under dry conditions, when spore discharge stops and the sporophore shrivels, each gill separates from below upwards into halves which curl backwards covering up the whole hymenium. Although this mechanism is remarkable and would seem to be associated with hymenium protection, its biological value may be doubted since many drought-resistant bracket fungi, such as *Polystictus versicolor* and *Stereum hirsutum,* seem to exist quite happily without any structural elaboration of this kind. In *Schizophyllum,* as in *Polystictus* and *Stereum,* the hairy upper surface of the dry fruit-body quickly absorbs rain and the sporophore is soon in a condition to liberate spores again.

Early in the present century Buller sealed, in separate evacuated glass tubes, a number of dry sporophores of *Schizophyllum commune.* Some still remain, but tubes opened after over fifty years have been found capable of shedding spores soon after wetting (Ainsworth, 1962). However, as with the drought-enduring Ascomycetes, it seems likely that in nature a sporophore lasts only for a single season.

There are a few Basidiomycetes in which the sporophores can not only survive under very dry conditions, but can also continue to liberate spores in spite of drought. These are the large woody perennial polypores particularly *Fomes fomentarius* and *Ganoderma applanatum.* The behaviour of these may be illustrated by a somewhat detailed consideration of *F. fomentarius.*

Buchwald and Hellmers (1946) obtained a cylindrical

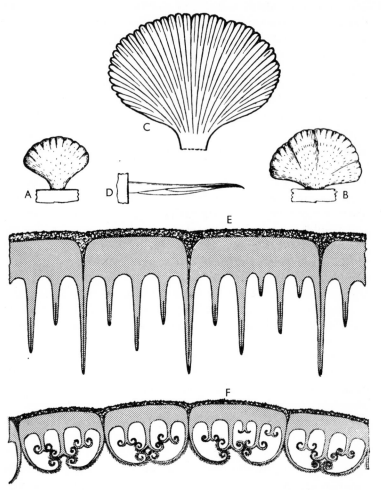

Fig. 49. *Schizophyllum commune.* A and B, fruit-bodies seen from above growing on wood, ×1. C and D, fruit-bodies seen from below and in section respectively, × 2. E, section of fruit-body during wet weather. F, section through fruit-body after drying, both × 12. After Buller (1909).

segment (about 60 cm high and 40 cm across) of a sycamore tree (*Acer pseudoplatanus*) bearing a large 2-year old fruit-body about 32 cm in diameter. In October this was placed, with the sporophore in its natural orientation, on a table in the corridor of the Department of Plant Pathology of the Royal Veterinary and Agricultural College, Copenhagen where the temperature was about 18°C. On 24 March the sporophore started to shed spores and during ten days there escaped visible, and photographably, white clouds, the average rate of spore liberation being 25000000000 a day. Another small specimen on a trunk of *Quercus robur* brought into the Department in April shed spores from 17 May to 14 July when observations ceased. Previously Buchwald (1938) had made similar observations on a specimen growing on poplar.

The observations suggest that *Fomes* can derive the necessary water from spore liberation either from the tissues of the sporophore or from the tree trunk which is penetrated by the vegetative mycelium of the fungus. With a large active specimen of *Fomes fomentarius* detached in May from the beech trunk on which it was growing, the present author found that spore discharge, although at first copious, ceased after two days in the laboratory. This suggests that the sporophore itself does not have a sufficient water-reserve to sustain discharge and that the major reserve is in the wood. In this connexion it should be realized that the water available in the wood is not merely that present as such, but also the water that can be liberated by the mycelium in the course of respiration by the oxidation of cellulose and other organic material. If the water in the wood is to be mobilized, an efficient conducting system must exist linking the fruit-body with this reserve. Very little is known about translocation in fungi. There do not seem to be separate channels concerned with the movement of water and of organic food as in higher plants. In general transport in fungi would seem to be quite inadequate to sustain the necessary water-flow to keep most fungal sporophores in a turgid condition during drought.

The water relations of the very common *Ganoderma applanatum* (see p. 138) seem to be exactly like those of *F. fomentarius*.

Isolated sporophores very soon cease to shed spores, but in the field sporophores can be seen liberating spores in rust-brown clouds even after a summer drought of over six-weeks' duration.

At this stage in our knowledge we can only outline the factors which allow *Fomes* and *Ganoderma* to continue their spore liberation in very dry weather. First, general water-loss from the sporophore is probably cut down by the existence of a hard, woody upper surface from which evaporation may be relatively slow; secondly, the long narrow hymenial tubes probably ensure that the basidia are maintained in a saturated atmosphere even though the outside air may be relatively dry; thirdly, the very broad connexion between the sporophore and the tree allows considerable hyphal connexions with the water-supply in the tree trunk; and fourthly, the hyphae leading from the trunk to the hymenial tubes appear to follow a fairly straight course and, being apparently relatively free from cross-walls, seem morphologically well suited to conduction.

Not only must the turgidity of the hymenial elements be maintained if discharge is to continue in Hymenomycetes, but the air in immediate contact with the hymenium must also be saturated or nearly so. Again there is little precise information about the effect of humidity on spore liberation. Some experiments with the shadow yeast *Sporobolomyces* may, however, be mentioned. A colony of this fungus producing ballistospores on aerial sterigmata may be considered as biologically equivalent to the hymenium of a toadstool and is much easier to handle experimentally. When a colony is subjected to alternating damp and dry air-streams operating for short periods, it is found that on change to dry conditions the rate of spore liberation immediately falls and recovers in the damp periods (Zoberi, 1964). Very probably the essential significance of hymenia being displayed in tubes or on the closely packed gills or spines in hymenomycete sporophores is related to the necessity of maintaining high humidity for spore discharge.

Although high humidity must apparently be maintained at the surface of an hymenium of discharging basidia, liquid water has a ruinous effect. An hymenium of this kind is quite different from a discomycete one of asci and paraphyses which is generally uninjured by wetting. It is to be remembered that most toadstools and bracket fungi are so constructed that the hymenia are well protected from rain.

Although most fungi which discharge their spores violently require an adequate water supply and essentially humid conditions, there are a few in which drying is a necessary

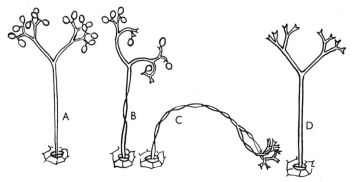

Fig. 50. *Peronospora tabacina*. A, conidiophore in damp air with attached conidia. B and C, changes on exposure to air of low humidity. D, recovery when returned to damp air. After Pinckard (1942).

preliminary to the effective liberation of spores. They are mostly conidial microfungi, and although dessication is needed if the spores are to be discharged, the actual development of sporulating structures requires the high humidity normal for fungal growth. In most of these organisms the spores ripen during the damp conditions of night-time and are discharged in the morning when the relative humidity of the air undergoes a rapid fall. There is thus a characteristic diurnal periodicity of spore liberation which will be discussed in a later chapter.

One kind of spore discharge involves sudden twisting of a hypha as drying takes place. The best-known example is *Peronospora tabacina*, the blue mould of tobacco (Fig. 50). The conidia are finely poised on the attenuated tips of a dichotomously branched conidiophore and the hygroscopic twirling of its main axis on drying scatters the spores (Pinckard, 1942).

Recently attention has been drawn (e.g. Meredith, 1963) to quite a number of examples amongst dematiaceous fungi (e.g. *Zygosporium* and *Deightoniella*) in which drying leads to the deflation of the cells of a conidium-bearing structure. Some of these distorted cells are thick-walled and are retained in a partially collapsed condition only because of the cohesion of the contained water and by its adhesion to the cell-walls. Eventually the water ruptures and the cells of the conidiophore, now containing a gas-phase, return instantly to the original shape, in doing so throwing off the associated spores (see p. 175).

Little is known concerning the water relations of fungi in which spores are not violently discharged, but in a study of a number of dry-spore moulds, including the common species *Trichothecium roseum*, it has been shown that spores are more freely blown off by winds of low than by those of high humidity (Zoberi, 1961).

The importance of rain for spore discharge has already been mentioned in connexion with the revival of drought-enduring Ascomycetes and Hymenomycetes. Further in Hymenomycetes there is the added necessity of protecting the actual hymenial surfaces from direct wetting by rain. However, there are other effects. Rain drops, if large enough, may by virtue of their kinetic energy be of considerable importance in spore liberation. Indeed, splash dispersal is becoming increasingly recognized as a significant process and the general principles of this have been considered in some detail by Gregory and his associates (Gregory *et al.*, 1959). They allowed water drops of definite size to fall onto a spore-suspension exposed as a film of known thickness on a glass slide. The sizes and scatter of the reflected droplets were studied and they were examined for contained spores. The slime-spore species, *Fusarium solani*, was generally the test organism. It was found that a drop 5 mm in diameter, about the largest raindrop possible, falling from a height of 7·4 m onto a spore-containing film 0·1 mm thick produced over 5000 reflected droplets of which more than 2000 carried spores. These droplets ranged from 5 μ to 2400 μ and, on the average, the distance to which they were scattered horizontally was 10–20 cm. The larger droplets fall back onto the substratum within a small fraction of a second, only the very small ones remaining suspended in the air. A study (Gregory *et al.*, 1959) has been made, using high-speed cinematography, of splash dispersal of conidia from a twig bearing abundant conidial stromata of *Nectria cinnabarina*. Large drops (5·0 mm diam.) falling from a height broke into thousands of droplets all of which carried spores. The conidia in such a species as this apparently rely entirely on rain-splash for their liberation.

Splash dispersal is unlikely to contribute very significantly to the air spora. However, large raindrops not only splash spores into the air; they have other mechanical effects. Thus in a crop infected with a fungal pathogen, heavy rain, particularly when it first begins to fall, may cause considerable stem vibration and leaf flutter which may assist spore liberation, and also the percussion waves associated with a heavy raindrop 5·0 mm in diameter moving with its steady terminal velocity of 920 cm/sec may blast dry spores, such as rust uredospores, into the air. Those who have studied the air spora have frequently noticed the temporary increase of dry-spore fungi at the onset of heavy rain. Later, however, rain markedly decreases the spore-content of the air as spores are combed out by the falling drops and brought to earth.

A good example of liberation of dry spores by rain drops is afforded by a study (Jarvis, 1962) of *Botrytis cinerea* in a raspberry plantation badly affected by grey mould of the fruit (Fig. 51). It seems that hygroscopic movements of the conidiophores release spores from organic contact with the conidiophores, but with insufficient vigour to cause actual discharge. Indeed, this distinction between release and take-off is significant in a number of plant pathogens, particularly rusts. In these probably the only uredospores which, at any moment, are in a condition to take off from a rusted wheat leaf are those which have already separated from their stalks and form a loose mass on the surface of the uredosorus. To return to *Botrytis*, it is found generally that spores become abundant in the air during the day-time periods of low relative humidity, but a heavy night-time shower may also result in a rapid build up of spore concentration. Jarvis remarks: 'There are two

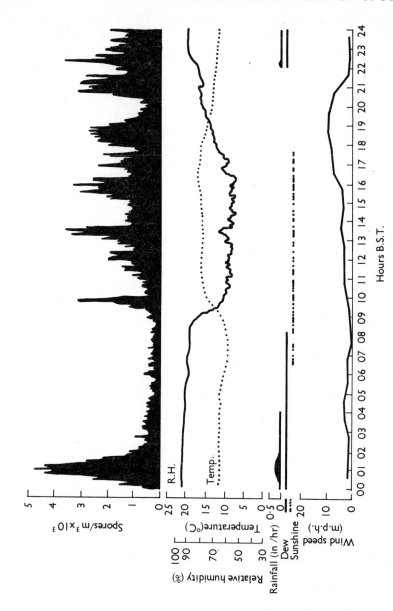

FIG. 51. *Botrytis cinerea* in raspberry plantation. Effect of rain at night and of low relative humidity by day on spore concentration of the air, 8 August 1960. After Jarvis (1962).

main effects of rain-splash on spore dispersal; dry spores are dispersed on air shock waves and turbulent currents, and composite projectiles of spores and splash droplets are formed, in which dry spores form a coating on the water droplets'.

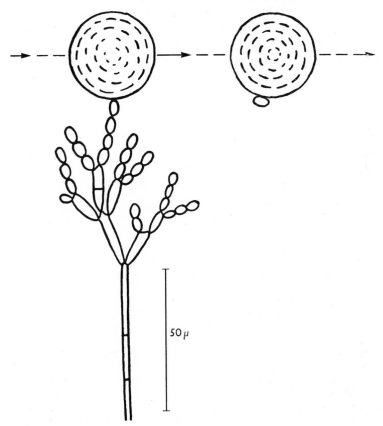

FIG. 52. Diagram of how drifting mist droplets might pick up spores of *Cladosporium herbarum*.

In some fungi there is a strong suggestion of specialization of structure in relation to dispersal by large raindrops. This is particularly striking in the splash-cup of the bird's nest fungus, *Cyathus* and in the drop-operated bellows of the puff-ball,

Lycoperdon. These mechanisms will be considered in a later chapter.

In considering the kinetic energy of raindrops in relation to spore liberation, attention has been concentrated on large drops with a high terminal velocity of fall, but water droplets moving horizontally at much lower speed may have some significance. It has been suggested in *Cercosporella herpotrichoides* that mist pick-up may be effective (Glynne, 1953) and this is possibly a subsidiary process in the take-off of spores in *Cladosporium* (Davies, 1959). Its general significance for spore liberation is in need of careful study (Fig. 52).

REFERENCES

AINSWORTH, G. C. (1962). Longevity of *Schizophyllum commune*. II. *Nature, Lond.* **195,** 1120–1121.

BUCHWALD, N. F. (1938). Om Sporenproduktionens størrelse hos Tøndersvampen. *Friesia* **2,** 42–69.

—— and HELLMERS, E. (1946). Fortsatte Iagttagelser over Sporefaeldning hos Tøndersvamp (*Polyporus fomentarius* (L.) Fr.). *Friesia* **3,** 212–216.

BULLER, A. H. R. (1909). *Researches on Fungi* Vol. I. London.

DAVIES, R. R. (1959). Detachment of conidia by cloud droplets. *Nature Lond.* **183,** 1695.

GLYNNE, M. D. (1953). Production of spores by *Cercosporella herpotrichoides*. *Trans. Br. mycol. Soc.* **36,** 46–51.

GREGORY, P. H. and STEDMAN, O. J. (1958). Spore dispersal in *Ophiobolus graminis* and other fungi of cereal foot rots. *Trans. Br. mycol. Soc.* **41,** 449–456.

GREGORY, P. H., GUTHRIE, E. J., and BUNCE, M. E. (1959) Experiments on splash dispersal of fungus spores. *J. gen. Microbiol.* **20,** 328–354.

HIRST, J. M., STOREY, I. F., WARD, E. C., and WILCOX, H. J. (1955). The origin of apple scab epidemics in the Wisbech area in 1953 and 1954. *Pl. Path.* **4,** 91–96.

HIRST, J. M. and STEDMAN, O. J. (1962). The epidemiology of apple scab (*Venturia inaequalis* [Cke.] Wint.) II. Observations on the liberation of ascospores. *Ann. appl. Biol.* **50,** 525–550.

INGOLD, C. T. (1946). Spore discharge in *Daldinia concentrica*. *Trans. Br. mycol. Soc.* **29,** 43–51.

—— (1948). The water-relations of spore discharge in *Epichloe*. *Trans. Br. mycol. Soc.* **31,** 277–280.

—— (1959). Jelly as a water-reserve in fungi. *Trans. Br. mycol. Soc.* **42,** 475–478.

—— (1960). Spore discharge in Pyrenomycetes. *Friesia* **6,** 148–163.

JARVIS, W. R. (1962). The dispersal of spores of *Botrytis cinerea* Fr. in a raspberry plantation. *Trans. Br. mycol. Soc.* **45,** 549–559.

MEREDITH, D. S. (1963). Further observations on the zonate eyespot fungus *Drechslera gigantea*, in Jamaica. *Trans. Br. mycol. Soc.* **46,** 201–207.

PINCKARD, J. A. (1942). The mechanism of spore dispersal in *Peronospora tabacina* and certain other downy mildew fungi. *Phytopathology* **32,** 505–511.

ZOBERI, M. H. (1961). Take-off of mould spores in relation to wind speed and humidity. *Ann. Bot.* **25,** 53–64.

—— (1964). Effect of temperature and humidity on ballistospore discharge. *Trans. Br. mycol. Soc.* **47,** 109–114.

95

V

RHYTHMS OF SPORE LIBERATION IN FUNGI

THE student of fungi is soon faced with evidence of rhythms. Some of these are of long period being conditioned by climate. British mycologists are accustomed to the annual cycle in the larger fungi giving a peak of fruit-body production in early autumn with a subsidiary one in May (Wilkins and Patrick, 1940), and their forays are arranged to coincide with these peaks. Rainfall and temperature seem to be the essential factors involved, there being no evidence of any photoperiodic determination of fruiting.

Again aerobiologists are very familiar with annual cycles in their catches of spores. As a result of extensive researches (Hyde and Williams, 1953) a clear picture is available for the mould *Cladosporium*, the commonest element in the air spora in almost every part of the world. In Britain there is a well-defined annual periodicity, with a summer maximum, probably reflecting the annual rhythm of temperature which so strongly affects mould development.

There seem to be very few relatively long-period rhythms in fungi unrelated to fluctuations in external factors. One example, however, is to be found in the ripening of *Sphaerobolus stellatus* as measured by the discharge of its glebal masses. When this species is grown on a suitable medium in continuous constant light and at a steady temperature, the daily discharge of glebal masses, which may go on for several months if the medium is deep enough, shows a periodicity with 10–12 days between peaks (Alasoadura, 1963). This corresponds closely with the time from fruit-body initiation to maturity and suggests that existing sporophores tend to inhibit the initiation of new ones until they have themselves discharged their glebal masses (Fig. 53).

The great majority of rhythms in fungi involve a 24-hour

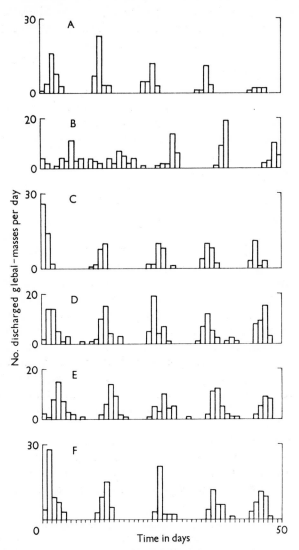

Fig. 53. *Sphaerobolus*. Daily glebal-mass discharge (starting from first day of discharge) in six cultures in continuous light (*c.* 1000 lux) at 20°C. Time before discharge started varied from 20 to 24 days. After Alasoadura (1963).

97

cycle and may be referred to as diurnal.† Spore liberation in particular is distinctly diurnal, and this is to be expected, because the factors which generally influence the take-off of spores themselves show a daily periodicity. Light has a day-time maximum and so has temperature, whereas the humidity of the air is highest at night. In a much more general manner, being apparent only if averaging is done over long periods, wind velocity tends to show a day-time peak. Again rainfall, which can profoundly affect spore liberation, may on the average show a diurnal periodicity, but this depends to a considerable extent on the locality.

The aerobiologists who study the concentration of spores in the air throughout the 24-hour period using a volumetric spore trap, particularly the Hirst model (Hirst, 1952), almost invariably observe a diurnal periodicity for each type of spore. Usually the results are reported in the form of a graph each point being a geometric mean, based on many days' observations, of the concentration of spores in the air at a particular time of day, the successive points on the graph being at hourly or 2-hourly intervals. For fungal spores Gregory (1961) recognizes a number of patterns of which there are three main ones: (1) the nocturnal pattern (e.g. *Sporobolomyces*); (2) the forenoon pattern (e.g. *Phytophthora infestans*); and (3) the afternoon pattern (e.g. *Cladosporium*) (Fig. 54). However, the distinction between the second and third is difficult to make and the really striking difference is between the day and the night sporas.

It must be emphasized that, although these patterns are probably in the main related to periods of spore liberation, this is not necessarily so. A diurnal rhythm of spores in the air might be observed unrelated to rhythmic take-off. Let us consider,

---

† The nomenclature of these rhythms is difficult. 'Diurnal' is an ambiguous word. It may refer to a whole 24-hour cycle, or it may be regarded as the opposite of 'nocturnal'. The rather unpleasant adjective 'circadian' has been used recently to denote a rhythm where one whole cycle is completed in about 24 hours, but without reference to whether the peak activity is during the day-time or the night-time. In this chapter this will not be used but 'diurnal' will be employed in this restricted sense.

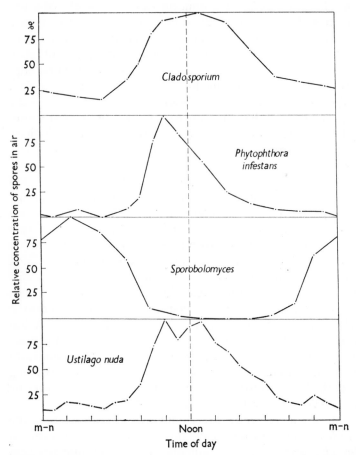

FIG. 54. Diurnal variations in spore content (Hirst trap determinations) expressed as percentage of peak geometric mean concentration. Curves for *Cladosporium* and *Phytophthora* based on observations on agricultural land at Rothamsted (Hirst, 1953); for *Sporobolomyces* curve on observations at Thorney Island, Chichester Harbour (Gregory and Sreeramulu, 1958); *Ustilago* curve on observations in infected barley field at Silwood Park, Berkshire (Sreeramulu, 1962).

99

say, the apothecium of a discomycete growing on the ground and discharging spores at a uniform rate to a height of a few millimetres. During the night in fair weather there is often a layer of still or laminar air, several centimetres in thickness in contact with the ground. Spores discharged into this would soon fall to the ground and would not be caught by a Hirst trap operating at the standard height of one metre. During the day, with the onset of turbulent conditions and the reduction of the laminar layer to a bare millimetre or less, discharged spores would be brought into the trapping area. Thus a periodicity might be recorded quite unconnected with periodic spore liberation.

Some rhythms in elements of the air spora are clearly related to periodicity of environmental factors. Thus Meredith (1961, 1962), working in banana plantations on *Deightoniella torulosa* (causing 'speckle' of the fruit) and *Cordana musae* (producing a minor leaf-spot), has found with both species a steep rise in the concentration of conidia in the air just after dawn associated with a sharp decline in the relative humidity of the air (Fig. 55). This can be related to the mechanism of spore take-off in both species involving, as it does, water-rupture as a result of drying in cells of the conidiophore. A similar diurnal periodicity has been observed for the spores of *Peronospora tabacina* in the air above tobacco fields affected by 'blue-mould'. Here the early morning maximum is no doubt connected with the twirling action of the conidiophores on drying which flings off the spores (Waggoner and Taylor, 1958).

In an intensive study Sreeramulu (1962) found that the maximum concentration of chlamydospores of loose smut of barley (*Ustilago nuda*) in the air above a heavily infected field occurred, on the average, during the midday hours (Fig. 54), the mean curves in two successive years being remarkably similar. This maximum appeared to be closely correlated with wind velocity which tends to be at its highest around this period of the day. Barley plants infected with *U. nuda* are normally a little taller than healthy ones, so that the smutted heads stand slightly above the general level. Further, diseased heads are light in weight and remain upright, whilst the normal stalks have relatively heavy heads and bend over away from the wind. Thus the chlamydospores, fully exposed as dry powdery masses, are in a particularly favourable position to be picked up and dispersed by wind (Fig. 56).

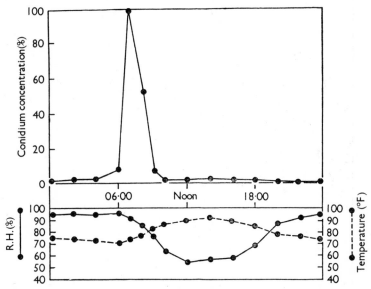

FIG. 55. Above: *Cordana musae;* mean diurnal periodicity of spore concentration in the air of a banana plantation; hourly values with peak concentration equated to 100. Below: corresponding mean hourly values for temperature and humidity. After Meredith (1962).

Probably the maximum for *Sporobolomyces* ballistospores observed in the small hours before dawn (Gregory and Sreeramulu, 1958) is associated principally with the high humidity necessary for spore discharge; the day-time diurnal periodicity of *Erysiphe* spores in the air is likely to be connected with light (Yarwood, 1936); whilst a similar periodicity for *Fomes annosus* basidiospores is more probably related to temperature (Sinclair, 1963).

Thus so far as the mean diurnal rhythms in elements of the air spora are concerned, different master factors appear to operate in different fungi. Further no doubt in a number of

Fig. 56. *Ustilago nuda*. Diagram of infected barley field. The smutted inflorescences of two infected stalks project erect above the healthy heads bent over in the wind (direction indicated by arrow.)

species the form of the mean diurnal periodicity curve is determined by the interaction of several different factors. Again these factors may operate in determining rhythmic ripening of spores, or more directly in the actual process of liberation.

We may now pass on to a consideration of diurnal periodicity of spore liberation in fungi which have been studied under experimental conditions often with a close control of the environment.

Considerable attention has been given to diurnal rhythms in spore liberation which are associated with light. We have seen that in *Sordaria fimicola*, provided the overall water-supply

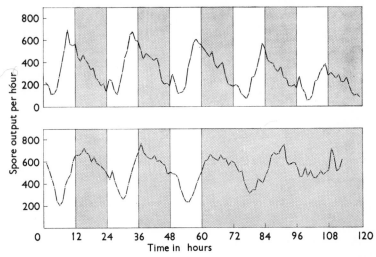

FIG. 57. *Sordaria verruculosa.* Course of spore discharge in two parallel cultures at 20°C and subjected to a régime of 12 hours' light and 12 hours of darkness. The second culture (lower curve) was finally placed in continuous darkness. Dark periods stippled. (Previously unpublished work but cf. Ingold and Marshall 1963.)

is assured, a very pronounced diurnal rhythm in spore discharge occurs, under conditions of 12 hours' light and 12 hours' darkness in each 24-hour period, with a maximum in day-time but with the peak activity reached long before the close of each light period. A similar rhythm has been reported in two other sordariaceous fungi, *Podospora curvula* (Ingold, 1933) and *P. setosa* (Callaghan, 1962). On the other hand in *Sordaria verruculosa* (Ingold and Marshall, 1963) with the same light: dark régime, more spores are usually discharged in the dark periods (Fig. 57). This, however, is not apparently the result of inhibition by light. Indeed, discharge is stimulated by change from darkness to light and inhibited by the reverse change, but there is an interval of 8–12 hours between the reception of the stimulus and maximum response. In the perithecial stroma of *Hypoxylon fuscum*, kept on wet filter paper at a fairly even temperature but with the normal light conditions of day and night, discharge is also essentially nocturnal (Fig. 58), but this seems to be the result of an immediate inhibitory effect of light on discharge even at very low intensities (Ingold and Marshall, 1963).

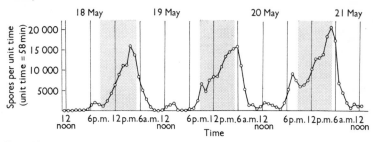

FIG. 58. *Hypoxylon fuscum.* Continuous record of rate of spore discharge from a stroma on wet filter paper, subjected to normal alternation of day and night in a north-facing room, the temperature range during this period being 17–19·5°C. After Ingold (1933).

Daldinia concentrica, very close to *Hypoxylon* taxonomically, is another nocturnal species, but in addition the rhythm is to some extent endogenous continuing after the periodic conditions have ceased to operate (Ingold and Cox, 1955). Subjected to 12 hours' light and 12 hours of darkness each day nearly all spores are shed in the dark, and this is also true of a stroma under natural conditions on a tree with the normal alternation of day and night. When a specimen is transferred to darkness at constant temperature and humidity, the periodic spore liberation continues for a number of days, sometimes for as many as twelve, but thereafter, although spores continue to be discharged, the rhythm is lost (Fig. 59). However, on return to periodic alternation of light and darkness, the old rhythm is immediately renewed. On transfer to continuous light from natural conditions, a stroma also retains its periodic spore discharge, but the periodicity is lost in two or three days,

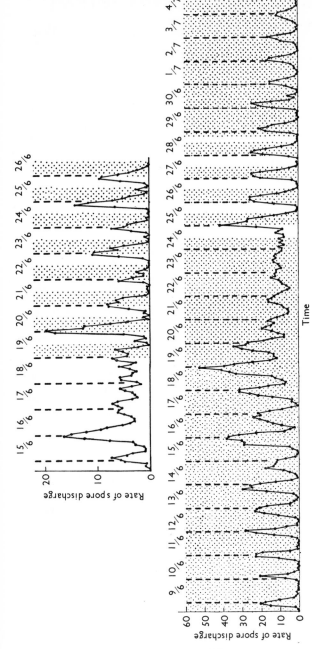

FIG. 59. *Daldinia concentrica*. Rate of spore discharge plotted against time. Upper graph: kept in continuous light for $4\frac{1}{2}$ days and thereafter placed under conditions of 12 hours' light and 12 hours of darkness in each day. Lower graph: different stroma kept in continuous darkness for 16 days, then placed under conditions of 12 hours' light and 12 hours' dark for several days, and then again placed in continuous darkness. Both stromata has previously been under normal field conditions. Temp. 21°C, light *c.* 1000 lux. Dotted regions indicate periods of darkness. Vertical interrupted lines show midnight positions. To convert the rate of discharge into number of spores trapped in each 2-hour period the figures on the ordinates must be multiplied by 100000. After Ingold (1960).

much more rapidly than in the dark. By subjecting a specimen to four six-hour periods each day with light alternating with darkness, a periodicity is soon produced with two maxima, one in each dark period and two minima corresponding with the periods of illumination in the course of 24 hours. When, however, a stroma so conditioned is placed in darkness, only the original night-time peak is 'remembered'. Attempts to produce a peak of discharge every other day by a régime of 24 hours' light followed by 24 hours of darkness and so on, have failed. With this régime the fungus still has its nocturnal peaks of maximum discharge with approximately a day between.

Although in Ascomycetes a light-conditioned rhythm of spore discharge appears to be common, it is apparently rare in Basidiomycetes. An example has, however, been described by Carpenter (1949) in *Pellicularia filamentosa* causing a leaf spot of *Hevea* rubber. This fungus in its spore discharge seems to resemble *Daldinia* particularly closely. With the normal alternation of day and night in Peru nearly all the spores are liberated in the dark, mainly before midnight. The periodicity of discharge seems to be endogenous for it goes on for several days in either continuous light or continuous darkness.

In many ways the story of periodicity in a culture of *Pilobolus* resembles that of a stroma of *Daldinia* except that the diurnal rhythm in *Pilobolus* involves a peak in discharge-rate during the day-time. It is important in any discussion of *Pilobolus* to emphasize that not all species behave in exactly the same way. In the two most exhaustive studies of this subject by Schmidle (1951) and by Uebelmesser (1954), *Pilobolus sphaerosporus* has been used, although in a few of her experiments Uebelmesser used *P. crystallinus* as well. *P. sphaerosporus* appears to be much easier to grow in the laboratory than other species. Further, in this, unlike other species, sporangiophores can develop in the complete absence of light, although sporulation is greatly stimulated by illumination.

With an alternation of 12 hours' light and 12 hours of darkness, humidity and temperature being kept constant, both German workers found a very pronounced peak of sporangial discharge about the middle of each light period and this

106

periodicity was retained for several days following transfer to continuous darkness (Fig. 60). Uebelmesser, as did Schmidle, investigated the effect on the rate of discharge of a considerable range of light: dark régimes of varying length. For example, with 6 hours' light alternating with 6 hours of darkness, peaks of discharge developed near the middle of each light period. On transfer to continuous darkness, however, although in the first 24 hours two peaks occurred at 12-hour intervals, following that the peaks were 24 hours apart. The same picture emerged with a régime of 4 hours' light: 4 hours' darkness. Peaks developed in the short light periods and, on transfer to uninterrupted darkness, these remained and were still 8 hours apart, but after 24 hours only a single daily peak persisted.

As with *Daldinia*, it does not seem possible to induce *Pilobolus* to adopt a 48-hour rhythm. Thus Uebelmesser found that whereas a régime of 1 hour light: 23 hours' darkness gave peaks of discharge activity a day apart, so did one involving 1 hour light: 47 hours' darkness.

In *P. sphaerosporus* a periodicity of temperature can also induce a rhythm in discharge of sporangia. Uebelmesser, using a dark-grown culture maintained at a 'ground' temperature of 15°C, gave it a daily treatment of one hour at 25°C. This led to a diurnal rhythm with a peak about half-way between each pair of warm periods. Further in a similar culture, but maintained at 25°C and given a daily hour at 15°C, the same type of rhythm developed with the peaks this time midway between the cold periods. In both cases the rhythm, having become established as a result of two or three days' treatment, persisted for at least four days at the uninterrupted 'ground' temperature. Again, as with light, a rhythm with two peaks in the 24-hour period could be induced by two separate hours at a high temperature (30°C) spaced 12 hours apart (Fig. 61). Following this if the culture was kept at a steady 'ground' temperature (20°C) the rhythm persisted with two peaks in the first 24 hours, but thereafter there was only one a day.

In both *Daldinia* and *Pilobolus* there seems to be a biological clock. In *Pilobolus* this can be set, by either light or temperature, to a 24-hour period, and once set the clock keeps

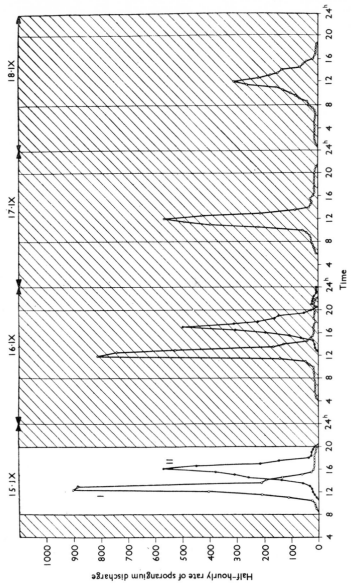

FIG. 60. *Pilobolus*. Half-hourly rate of sporangium discharge from cultures of *P. sphaerosporus* (white dots) and *P. crystallinus* (black dots) plotted against time. Cultures in régime of 12 hours' light and 12 hours' dark from 13.IX up to 20 hours on 15.IX; thereafter continuous darkness. Curve for 14.IX. as for 15.IX. After Uebelmesser (1954).

time for several days without the necessity for outside re-setting.

Sphaerobolus stellatus is another fungus exhibiting, in the discharge of its glebal masses, a diurnal periodicity clearly

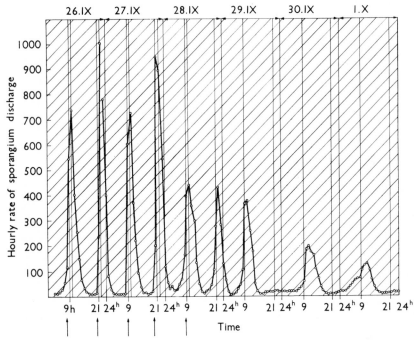

FIG. 61. *Pilobolus sphaerosporus.* Hourly rate of sporangium discharge from a culture kept in the dark at a general temperature of 20°C raised to 30°C for one hour twice in 24 hours (at 9 hours and 21 hours). Last high temperature treatment at 9 hours on 28.IX. After Uebelmesser (1954).

related to alternation of light and darkness. In this gastero-mycete a soft adhesive spore-containing glebal mass, about the size of a small mustard seed, is catapulted from the ripe opened sporophore to a distance of up to several metres. Further, unlike most Gasteromycetes, it can be grown easily in pure culture in the laboratory. On an appropriate medium and with other environmental conditions properly adjusted, it fruits abundantly (Alasoadura, 1963). Initiation of fruit-bodies takes place only if the light intensity is sufficiently high and then only if the temperature is below a limiting value of approximately 25°C. Not only is light absolutely necessary for the initiation and early growth of sporophores, but light also strongly stimulates their further development, although the minimum effective intensity steadily falls. The very last stage of ripening of the spherical sporophore, which is about 2 mm in diameter, may actually be retarded by light. A few hours before discharge the sporophore undergoes a stellate opening, the peridium separating into two little toothed cups, one inside the other, in contact only near the points of the teeth. The glebal mass, submerged in an aqueous fluid, lies snugly but loosely within the inner cup. It is by the sudden eversion of this turgid inner peridial cup that the discharge is effected. The actual process of discharge involving this eversion appears to be independent of conditions of illumination.

An extensive study of periodic discharge has been made by Friederichsen and Engel (1960). Under conditions of 12 hours' light: 12 hours' dark each day discharge is entirely in the light with a peak rate in the middle of each period (Fig. 62). With a light: dark régime of 4:20 hours each day, discharge is still diurnal, but no discharge occurs in the light periods and practically all the glebal masses are catapulted off within an hour or two of transfer to darkness. Again with alternating days of light and dark, discharge is almost limited to the dark days.

Engel and Friederichsen (1964) have found, further, that when a fruiting culture which has been grown in continuous light is transferred to continuous darkness, over a period of some ten days there is evidence of a diurnal rhythm of glebal-mass discharge, in spite of the fact that during two or three days around the middle of the period discharge temporarily ceases. This seems to indicate a natural tendency in a culture to diurnal rhythm apparently unrelated to previous periodicity of illumination.

It is difficult to suggest a completely satisfactory theory to account for the curious facts of periodicity in *Sphaerobolus*.

However, it is probable that the solution to the problem lies in the action of light during the final hours of maturation of the fruit-body, before it actually opens prior to the discharge of its glebal mass. It seems that at this stage stimulation by light gives place to retardation (Alasoadura, 1963). Thus a dark period allows a crop of almost ripe sporophores to reach

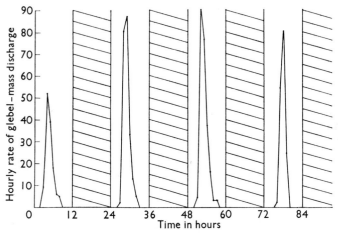

FIG. 62. *Sphaerobolus.* Hourly rate of glebalmass discharge plotted against time in a régime of 12 hours' light and 12 hours' darkness (shaded periods). After Friederichsen and Engel (1960).

a ready-to-discharge condition, but delays the further development of slightly younger fruit-bodies. If the dark period is not too prolonged actual discharge will then occur during the subsequent light period when more sporophores will mature to the almost ripe condition. If however, the dark period is a long one, of say 20 hours duration, discharge will occur during it.

Although the theory of change of sensitivity to light during the final, pre-opening, stages of maturation of the sporophore does account, in a general way, for the normal periodicity picture and does explain the overall pattern of discharge in certain unusual alternations of dark and light periods, it fails fully to account for the distribution of the rate of discharge within the dark periods when these alternations are in operation.

Another example of the importance of both dark and light periods in the maintenance of a diurnal rhythm of spore liberation is afforded by *Pyricularia oryzae*. This causes 'blast' of rice, but although in nature it is a parasite, it will grow and

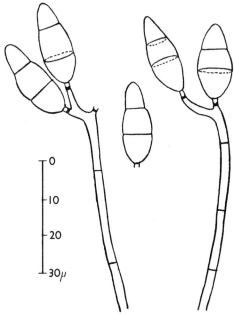

FIG. 63. *Pyricularia oryzae.* Two conidiophores and a liberated conidium

sporulate fairly well on nutrient agar in the laboratory. Spores are set free only if the air is saturated or nearly so, and it seems likely that an active discharge mechanism is involved. Spores fall regularly from an undisturbed inverted culture and this strongly suggests an active process. The elongated three-celled conidium is attached to its conidiophore by a minute stalk cell. This appears to undergo an equatorial splitting so that one half of it remains on the conidiophore and the other on the liberated spore (Fig. 63). It is difficult to envisage regular spore release under humid conditions unless the sticky liquid connection at the ruptured stalk-cell is broken violently. Probably the stalk-cell bursts with just sufficient vigour to set the spore free. This process is, however, only inferred. If the distance of discharge is a mere fraction of a millimetre, it would be difficult to demonstrate.

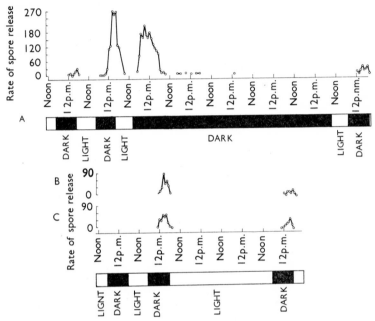

FIG. 64. *Pyricularia oryzea*. Results of three experiments showing rate of spore discharge plotted against time. The light-dark régime is indicated. Spores are set free in dark periods following light periods. After Barksdale and Asai (1961).

Barksdale and Asai (1961) have studied the release of spores from rice leaves infected with this fungus. The process is nocturnal under conditions resembling the natural alternation of day and night. When, however, *Pyricularia oryzae* is subjected to continuous darkness discharge ceases after about twelve hours and is not resumed again in darkness until there has been a prior period of illumination (Fig. 64). Similarly spore liberation ceases in continuous light. It would thus seem that both the dark and the light periods exert an influence on sporulation leading to discharge.

Diurnal rhythms in spore discharge are, perhaps, often to be regarded only as special cases of such rhythms in sporulation. These are familiar to all mycologists if only as concentric zoning in cultures. Usually day-time zones of intense sporulation alternate with night-time zones where fewer spores are formed. Nearly always zonation is related to the natural diurnal alternation of light and dark (e.g. Hall, 1933; Sagromonsky, 1952 (*a*), (*b*)), although temperature alternation may also sometimes induce zoning (Hafiz, 1951) and occasionally the same effect is brought about as an endogenous rhythm without periodicity in external conditions being involved (Brandt, 1953).

Since diurnal rhythms of spore liberation are so common, it is natural to consider if they have any biological significance. In a fungus which is wind-dispersed a rhythm involving day-time discharge may well have survival value because of the relatively high wind velocities associated with the daily development of thermal turbulence. On the other hand nocturnal spore discharge might be an advantage for a stem of leaf pathogen with spores which quickly lose their viability and depend on infection drops for germination. Discharge in such a fungus might be timed, as it were, to coincide with the nightly occurrence of dew. Again in such a fungus as *Pilobolus* the shooting of sporangia during the daytime ensures that it takes place at a time when the spore projectiles can be aimed by the quickly-adjusting phototropic response of the sporangiophores which, in temperate latitudes, helps to scatter the discharged sporangia over the grass surrounding the dung. However, generally speaking it is by no means easy to suggest the possible biological value of rhythms of spore discharge.

REFERENCES

ALASOADURA, S. O. (1963). Fruiting in *Sphaerobolus* with special reference to light. *Ann. Bot.* **27,** 125–145.

BARKSDALE, T. H. and ASAI, G. N. (1961). Diurnal spore release of *Piricularia oryzae* from rice leaves. *Phytopathology* **51,** 313–317.

RHYTHMS OF SPORE LIBERATION IN FUNGI

BRANDT, W. H. (1953). Zonation in a prolineless strain of *Neurospora*. *Mycologia* **45**, 194–208.

CALLAGHAN, A. A. (1962). Observations on perithecium production and spore discharge in *Pleurage setosa*. *Trans. Br. mycol. Soc.* **45**, 249–254.

CARPENTER, J. B. (1949). Production and discharge of basidiospores of *Pellicularia filamentosa* (Pat.) Rogers on *Hevea* rubber. *Phytopathology* **39**, 980–985.

ENGEL, H. and FRIEDERICHSEN, I. (1964). Der Abschluss der Sporangiolen von *Sphaerobolus stellatus* (Thode) Pers. in kontinuierlicher Dunkelheit. *Planta* **61**, 361–370.

FRIEDERICHSEN, I. and ENGEL, H. (1960). Der Abschussrhythmus der Fruchtkörper von *Sphaerobolus stellatus* (Thode) Pers. *Planta* **55**, 313–326.

GREGORY, P. H. (1961). *The microbiology of the atmosphere*. London.

—— and SREERAMULU, T. (1958). Air spora of an estuary. *Trans. Br. mycol. Soc.* **41**, 145–156.

HAFIZ, A. (1951). Cultural studies of *Ascochyta rabiei* with special reference to zonation. *Trans. Br. mycol. Soc.* **34**, 259–269.

HALL, M. P. (1933). An analysis of the factors controlling the growth form of certain fungi, with special reference to *Sclerotinia (Monilia) fructigena* *Ann. Bot.* **47**, 543–578.

HIRST, J. M. (1952). An automatic volumetric spore trap. *Ann. appl. Biol.* **39**, 257–265.

—— (1953). Changes in atmospheric spore content: diurnal periodicity and the effects of weather. *Trans. Br. mycol. Soc.* **36**, 375–393.

HYDE, H. A. and WILLIAMS, D. A. (1953). The incidence of *Cladosporium herbarum* in the outdoor air at Cardiff, 1949–50. *Trans. Br. mycol. Soc.* **36**, 260–266.

INGOLD, C. T. (1933). Spore discharge in Ascomycetes. I. Pyrenomycetes. *New Phyt.* **32**, 175–196.

—— (1960). Spore discharge in Pyrenomycetes. *Friesia* **6**, 148–163.

—— and COX, V. J. (1955). Periodicity of spore discharge in *Daldinia*. *Ann. Bot.* **29**, 201–209.

INGOLD, C. T. and MARSHALL, B. (1963). Further observations on light and spore discharge in certain Pyrenomycetes. *Ann. Bot.* **27**, 481–491.

MEREDITH, D. S. (1961). Fruit-spot ('speckle') of Jamaican bananas caused by *Deightoniella torulosa* (Syd.) Ellis IV. Further observations on spore dispersal. *Ann. appl. Biol.* **49**, 488–496.

—— (1962). Dispersal of conidia of *Cordana musae* (Zimm.) Höhnel in Jamaican banana plantations. *Ann. appl. Biol.* **50**, 263–267.

SAGROMONSKY, H. (1952a). Der Einflusz des Lichtes auf die rhythmische Konidienbildung von *Penicillium*. *Flora* **139**, 300–313.

—— (1952b). Lichtinduzierte Ringbildung bei Pilzen II. *Flora* **139**, 560–564.

SCHMIDLE, A. (1951). Die Tagesperiodizität der asexuellen Reproduktion von *Pilobolus sphaerosporus*. *Arch. Mikrobiol.* **16**, 80–100.

RHYTHMS OF SPORE LIBERATION IN FUNGI

SINCLAIR, W. A. (1963). Effects of temperature and moisture upon daily and seasonal patterns of basidiospore dispersal by *Fomes annosus*. *Phytopathology* **53**, 352.

SREERAMULU, T. (1962). Aerial dissemination of barley loose smut (*Ustilago nuda*). *Trans. Br. mycol. Soc.* **45**, 373–384.

UEBELMESSER, E. R. (1954). Über den endonomen Tagesrhythmus der Sporangienträgerbildung von *Pilobolus*. *Arch. Mikrobiol.* **20**, 1–33.

WAGGONER, P. E. and TAYLOR, G. S. (1958). Dissemination by atmospheric turbulence: spores of *Peronospora tabacina*. *Phytopathology* **48**, 46–51.

WILKINS, W. H. and PATRICK, S. H. M. (1940). The ecology of the larger fungi IV. The seasonal frequency of grassland fungi with special reference to the influence of environmental factors. *Ann. appl. Biol.* **27**, 17–34.

YARWOOD, C. E. (1936). The diurnal cycle of the powdery mildew *Erysiphe polygoni*. *J. agric. Res.* **52**, 645–657.

VI

TOADSTOOLS, THEIR FORM AND FUNCTION

THE toadstool, an hymenomycete fruit-body with a circular cap and central stipe, is probably the commonest kind of reproductive structure amongst Higher Fungi. Although the great majority of toadstools are gill-bearing, many are polypores, some are hydnoid and a few are thelephoroid.

FIG. 65. *Agaricus arvensis*. Diagram of the three phases: feeding mycelium in the soil, sporophore, and dispersing spore cloud. After Buller (1909).

The sporophore or fruit-body is essentially a structure concerned with the production and liberation of spores. It is mostly quite short-lived in contrast to the often perennial nature of the mycelium which is usually hidden away within the nutrient substratum. But in a total picture of a fungus, as pointed out by Large (1961), there is also a third phase, the spore cloud. Buller's beautiful drawing (Fig. 65) illustrates, for a horse mushroom, the three essential phases: vegetative mycelium, sporophore, and dispersing spore cloud.

Our understanding of toadstools as functional entities derives mostly from the morphological and histological studies of Buller (1909–31). Covering the gills, teeth, or spines, or lining the hymenial tubes of the sporophore is a layer of basidia, sometimes interspersed with cells of a different nature, although in many hymenia what have formerly been regarded as paraphyses may simply be young basidia (Fig. 66, D). The disposition of the

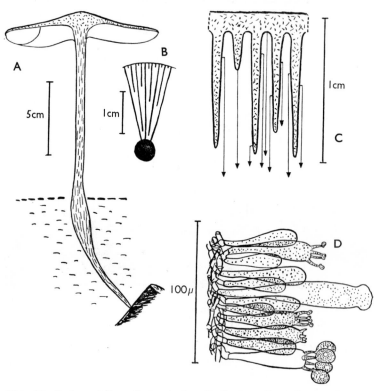

FIG. 66. *Oudemansiella radicata*. A, longitudinal section of sporophore; a pseudorhiza, attached to buried wood, extends upwards into the stipe which bears the pileus. B, sector of undersurface showing gill pattern; the black disk is the stipe seen in transverse section at gill level. C, tangential vertical section of cap showing vertical gills and the trajectories of some escaping spores. D, small portion of hymenium with basidia at various stages of development and a single cystidium.

hymenial surface is very largely conditioned by the behaviour of the basidium which must, therefore, be considered in some detail.

The structure and later developmental history of a typical hymenomycete basidium is illustrated in Fig 67. The basidia occur at right angles to the hymenial surface with their

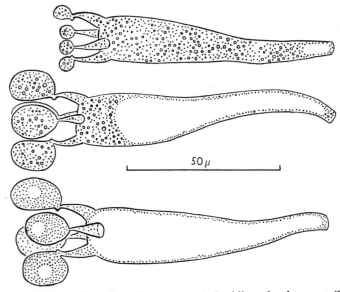

FIG. 67. *Oudemansiella radicata*. Later stages in basidium development. The enlargement of a vacuole in the base of the basidium drives the protoplasm by 'piston' action into the enlarging spores.

longitudinal axes parallel, and this means that most basidia are more or less horizontal Usually the basidium bears four spores each perched asymmetrically at the end of a fine, tapering sterigma Very near to its junction with the sterigma the spore has a minute projection or hilum. That the tip of this is at an appreciable distance from the actual point of spore attachment is more apparent in some species than in others. It is particularly obvious, for example, in *Calocera cornea*, one of the gelatinous Basidiomycetes, and in species of *Russula*.

The four spores of the basidium are violently discharged in succession to a distance of 0·1–0·2 mm. It is important to appreciate that the basidium is a very short-range spore gun, in striking contrast to the ascus with a range usually about 10 mm but varying from 2–600 mm.

Just before a basidiospore is discharged from its sterigma, a drop of liquid suddenly makes its appearance at the hilum, in the course of a few seconds grows to a definite size (2–5 μ diam.) small in comparison with that of the spore, and then the

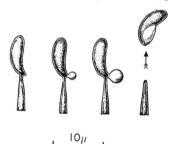

LFIG. 68. *Calocera cornea*. A single sterigma with its basidiospore illustrating drop exudation at the hilum and discharge. After Buller (1922).

spore is shot away carrying the drop with it (Fig. 68). Immediately following discharge the sterigma appears essentially unchanged in form and is apparently closed at its tip for no liquid exudes. Once the first has gone the remaining spores of the basidium are shot away one after the other usually with an interval of at least several seconds between. After the loss of its spores the basidium, though at first fully turgid, soon collapses and undergoes autolysis.

A spore placed asymmetrically on a sterigma and discharged violently immediately following drop-production at the hilum has conveniently been called a 'ballistospore' (Derx, 1948). Not all ballistospores are basidiospores, and not all basidiospores are ballistospores. Thus the aerial conidia of the very abundant 'mirror yeasts' (Sporobolomycetaceae) are ballistospores, whilst the basidiospores of Gasteromycetes are not.

The nature of the discharge mechanism still remains uncertain. There are some major theories. First it has been suggested that the spore is discharged by a water-squirting mechanism as in *Pilobolus*, but on a microscopic scale. If this occurs it would be expected that a drop of exuding liquid would be visible at the tip of the sterigma just after discharge, but that is not to be seen. Further, if a water-squirting mechanism does operate the sterigma must presumably be immediately self-sealing so that the turgor of the unicellular basidium is retained for the discharge of subsequent spores. The water-squirting theory has, however, been given new life by the observations of Müller (1954) on the liberation of ballistospores in the mirror yeast *Sporobolomyces*. He filmed the whole process though, unfortunately, not at ultra-high speed. Although normally the spore and its exuded drop were seen to leave the sterigma simultaneously, he found that, as a rare occurrence, the drop suddenly disappeared, presumably having been discharged, leaving the spore behind and still attached (Fig. 69). Müller assumes that drop-exudation is, in fact, at the actual junction of the spore with its sterigma, and that the drop is squirted away by hydrostatic pressure carrying the spore with it. The difficulty in accepting Müller's interpretation of the observed events is that Buller's extensive observations on a wide range of ballistospores indicate clearly that exudation of the drop is from the hilum which is a part of the spore and not a part of the sterigma.

Another theory is that discharge is due to a sudden rounding off at a cross-wall separating the spore from its sterigma. If this is correct, the process would be similar to that occurring in *Entomophthora coronata* (Martin, 1925) (Fig. 70) and *Sclerospora philippinensis* (Weston, 1923). A difficulty for this theory is the paucity of evidence for the existence at the moment of discharge of a cross-wall separating sterigma and spore. However, in the rust *Gymnosporangium nidus-avis*, Prince (1943) was able to see and photograph such a cross-wall. On the basis of his observations he strongly supported the theory that basidiospore discharge is due to sudden rounding off of spore and sterigma at a previously flat junction (Fig. 69). A striking feature of ballistospores, which makes them fairly readily identifiable as such by the aerobiologist, is the hilum, the minute projection from the tip of which drop-exudation occurs during the process of discharge. The term 'hilum' is, however, more suitable for an actual attachment scar. The minute projection of the ballistospore might, perhaps, be called more appropriately a

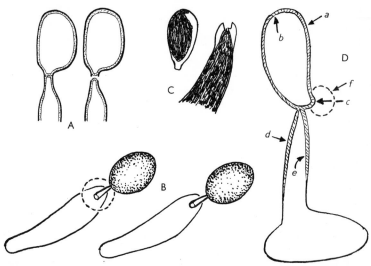

FIG. 69. A, *Gymnosporangium nidus-avis*: diagram of basidiospore and the tip of its sterigma before and just after discharge (after Prince, 1943). B, *Sporobolomyces salmonicola*: drawings made from two neighbouring frames of a film: on left, drop (outline dashed) has appeared at hilum and reached its full size; on right (1/64 sec later) drop has disappeared (after photographs by Müller, 1954). C, *Cronartium ribicola*: drawings from electronmicrographs of sections: left, spore with hilum: right, section of sterigma showing cup-like depression in tip (after photograph by Dr. Bega). D, *Sporobolomyces*: vegetative cell, sterigma, and spore: *a*, outer spore-membrane; *b*, inner spore-membrane; *c*, hilum; *d*, outer sterigma-membrane; *e*, inner sterigma-membrane; *f*, bubble (after Olive, 1964). A, B, C, and D all highly magnified.

'basal peg' or 'pseudohilum' since the spore is not normally attached by the tip of this structure to its sterigma.

Dr. Bega has, however, recently observed that in the basidiospore of *Cronartium ribicola* the hilum is a true one, and, indeed, the earlier figures of Prince also indicate that this is so in

Gymnosporangium (Fig. 69). Dr. Bega has gone further and demonstrated in an electron-micrograph that the sterigma has a deep cup in its tip in which the hilum presumably rests (Fig. 69).†

A third suggestion is that the surface energy of the exuded drop is in some way used for discharge (Ingold, 1939). There is little evidence, however, to support this idea, except that there does seem to be sufficient energy available from this

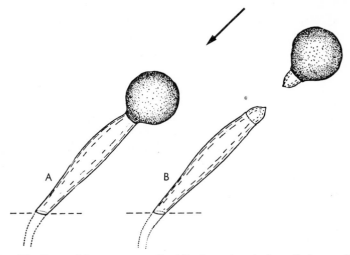

FIG. 70. *Entomophthora coronata.* Conidiophore just before discharge (A) and at moment of discharge (B). Arrow indicates direction of incident light. ×500

source. However, it is difficult to envisage how it might be mobilized.

Olive (1964) has developed a completely new outlook on the problem of ballistospore discharge. According to him the 'drop', exuded at the hilium heralding discharge, is really a bubble which when it bursts violently dislodges the spore from its sterigma. He figures the ripe spore and the sterigma with a double wall and claims that gas, probably respiratory carbon

† Personal communication by Dr. R. V. Bega U.S. Dept. Agriculture, California.

dioxide, accumulates between the two layers (Fig. 69, D). A weakening of the outer membrane in the region of the hilum results in a spherical blister or bubble being blown there which eventually bursts discharging the spore. If this picture is correct a number of abnormal occurrences sometimes observed during discharge are explicable, but there are certain difficulties. In particular there is the observation of Buller, apparently often repeated, that the 'drop' is still to be observed and undiminished in size on the discharged spore. This observation is apparently confirmed by Müller (1954) in his film of *Sporobolomyces* in which a significant volume of liquid is shown associated with the ballistospore immediately after it has left the sterigma.

Buller has considered the trajectory of a basidiospore discharged from a horizontal basidium (Fig. 71). This is the most usual orientation for a basidium because the hymenial surfaces tend to be roughly vertical. The flight path figured would probably only be realized perfectly under conditions of almost complete stillness. Nevertheless, this is probably the normal state of affairs within the narrow vertical hymenial tubes of polypores, between the closely-packed gills of an agaric or amongst the crowded teeth of a hydnoid fungus. The trajectory, named by Buller a "sporabola" (Buller, 1909), is given by the equation:

$$y = \left(\frac{V^2}{g} - \log_e \left(1 - \frac{x}{X} \right) - \frac{x}{X} \right)$$

where V = the terminal velocity of fall of the spore.
X = maximum horizontal distance of projection,
g = the acceleration due to gravity,
y = the vertical distance of a point on the trajectory below the point of liberation, and
x = the horizontal distance from the vertical axis of this point.

Essentially the sporabola consists of an almost horizontal part completed in a minute fraction of a second, and of a vertical part where the spore falls relatively slowly according to Stokes' Law (Fig. 72).

The sporabola seems at first sight to be a somewhat improbable trajectory for a discharged object to follow. However, it can, in fact, easily be imitated by striking an air-filled toy balloon horizontally from the top of a table. Both with the microscopic spore and with the balloon it is the over-riding importance of air resistance which determines the unusual form of the trajectory.

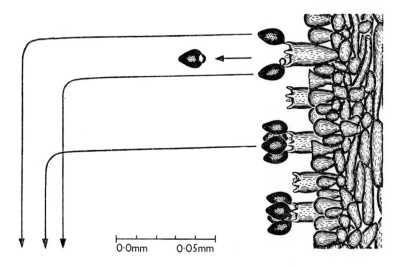

Fig. 71. *Panaeolus campanulatus*. Part of the hymenium in vertical section of the gill showing spore discharge. Lines with arrows show trajectories of spores. After Buller (1922).

In considering the first part of the path followed by the liberated spore, it must be borne in mind that there is practically no information about the exact direction of discharge. It is not known if a basidiospore is normally shot in a direction parallel with the longitudinal axis of the basidium or at an angle to it. Further, nothing is known about the constancy of the direction of discharge.

The second part of the sporabola, determined by gravitational fall, has been considered to be vertical. However, this is completely true only for spherical particles. It has been calculated that a microscopic ellipsoidal particle falling in such a viscous fluid as air, tends to retain its original orientation and further that it falls vertically only if one of its three

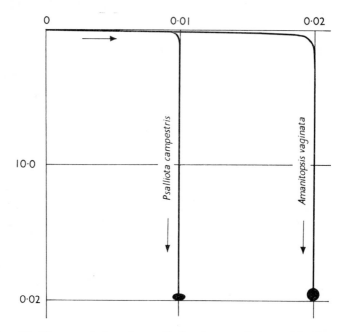

Fig. 72. The sporobolas of two kinds of spore discharged horizontally. The spores, drawn to scale, and shown on the base line. The scale is in centimetres. After Buller (1909).

axes of rotation is vertical. Otherwise the ellipsoidal particle should fall at an angle to the vertical. With random orientation of particles and considering the type of ellipsoidal spore with its two shorter axes equal, the mean divergence from the vertical increases with the length to breadth ratio as shown in Fig. 73.†

† Personal contribution by Dr. A. Fonda who, when a research officer of the National Coal Board, carried out an exhaustive study of the mathematics of falling ellipsoidal particles.

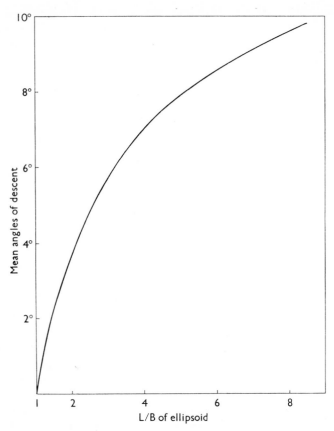

Fig. 73. Mean angle of descent for falling ellipsoidal particles (with two short axes of ellipsoid equal) plotted against length: breadth ratio of the ellipsoid. Based on tables by Dr. Fonda (private communication).

The only quantitative experimental study of vertical fall of ellipsoidal spores was carried out by Yarwood and Hazen (1942). They used the conidia of *Erysiphe graminis* which have smooth walls, do not collapse on drying and are nearly three times as long as broad (32 × 13 μ). Their rate of fall in still air was found to be approximately 1·2 cm/sec. The spores were observed through a horizontal microscope as they fell down a glass tube 77 cm long and 0.7 cm wide. Yarwood and Hazen actually used several different methods to determine the orientation of the spores during their fall and all gave the same result, namely that the spores were either vertical or horizontal and apparently never assumed an intermediate position. Out of a total of 1068 conidia considered 545 were vertical as they fell and 523 horizontal. This, perhaps, is not so unexpected as might at first be thought. If the spores as they enter the long tube are randomly oriented it might be expected that those in which no axis is vertical would be diverted to one side and deposited on the walls of the tube, leaving only the vertical and horizontal spores, which might be expected to be equally numerous, to complete their downward journey.

Yarwood and Hazen do, however, remark that 'in one test using a narrower tube ..., all the conidia were found in a vertical position'. Gregory (1961) makes the useful suggestion that in the narrow tube 'the vertical position was due to drag at the wall boundary'. Clearly more experimental work is needed on the behaviour of elongated spores as they drop under the influence of gravity in still air and on how they are affected in their fall by a vertical surface close to them. We shall return to the question of the fall of spores in the inter-lamellar spaces or down the middle of an hymenial tube at a later stage.

Clearly the distance apart of gills in an agaric must exceed that of basidiospore discharge, otherwise the spores, which are very adhesive, would become impacted on the opposite hymenial surface and escape from the sporophore would be impossible. Also, in all but such exceptionally rigid sporophores as those of *Ganoderma applanatum*, there must be a margin of safety, and in fact hymenial surfaces tend to be several times wider apart than the range of the basidium as a spore gun would seem to require (Fig. 66).

Spores, shot from the hymenia into the spaces between the gills, fall under gravity and on emerging below the cap are well placed for aerial dispersal. In practically all agarics the whole gill surface ripens simultaneously and at any one time spores are being discharged from every part of it, except for a fine-grain mosaic of ripening that occurs in some species (e.g.

Panaeolus campanulatus) and which has no relevance for the present argument. Spores may, therefore, have to fall a significant distance between opposite gill surfaces before emerging into the free air below the cap. Thus if escape is to be successful the gills must be vertical. This orientation is brought about by growth responses to gravity.

The stipe is negatively geotropic and this ensures that the gills, hanging below the pileus, are roughly vertical. In some toadstools, such as *Agaricus campestris*, this is the only tropistic reaction of the stipe, but in others, particularly in lignicolous and coprophilous species, the stipe may, during its earlier stages of development, exhibit a strong positive phototropism. It had been suggested that as this dies out it is succeeded by negative geotropism. However, in his analysis of a stipitate polypore (*Polyporus brumalis*), Plunkett (1961) has shown that throughout its development the sporophore is responsive to both light and gravity. The phototropism is not lost, but in the later stages the developing pileus shades the perceptive region, the impact of light is thus reduced and response to gravity becomes dominant.

The coarse adjustment of the gills in an agaric is secured by the negative geotropism of the stipe and is usually supplemented by a fine adjustment. The individual gill is positively geotropic. If a pileus is tilted so that the gills are no longer quite vertical, each undergoes growth movements until it is again in the vertical plane.

This fine adjustment of hymenial surfaces is apparently a general feature of agarics. But it does not occur in the specialized genus *Coprinus*, in species of which the gill ripens progressively from its free edge towards the pileus tissue. In any minute area of the hymenium all the basidia are at approximately the same stage of development and once the spores are discharged no more basidia develop there. Further, the old exhausted hymenium at the free gill-edge is removed by a process of autodigestion which characterizes most species of *Coprinus*. The result is that spores never have more than a fraction of a millimetre to fall between opposing gills before emerging. Here the necessity for exact orientation of the gills is not so great and in fact they are not geotropic.

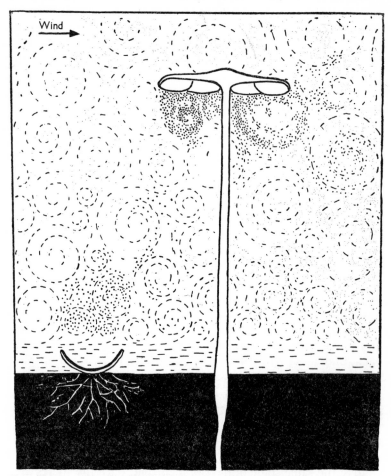

FIG. 74. A cup-fungus (*Peziza* sp.) and an agaric (*Oudemansiella radicata*). The ground is shown black. Above this is the laminar air (horizontal dashes) and on top of this the turbulent air (dashes in eddies). The *Peziza* has just discharged a puff of spores through the laminar air into the turbulent region. From the pileus of the agaric spores are steadily dropping into the turbulent air.

Although in gill-bearing toadstools the fine adjustment of hymenial surfaces by positive geotropism is possible, this is not so in a *Boletus* where the hymenial tubes, being knit together in a common system, have no power of individual response to gravity. On the other hand in *Hydnum* positive geotropism of the separate hymenial teeth readily occurs.

In a toadstool it is necessary for the hymenial surfaces to retain their vertical orientation from minute to minute. A spore-liberating mechanism of this kind cannot afford to sway in the wind. This leads to a consideration of the essential functions of the stipe. First, as we have just seen, by its response to external stimuli it helps in positioning the pileus and in the proper adjustment of its hymenial surfaces. Secondly, by elevating the cap above the ground it ensures that the spores are dropped into air which is often likely to be in a turbulent condition conducive to dispersal (Fig. 74). Thirdly, by its solidity it maintains the gills in a constantly correct position for spore liberation.

In solid objects that vary in size but not in form, three-dimensional features, such as volume, vary as the cube, and two-dimensional features, such as area, as the square of the linear measurements. Thus on doubling the dimensions of a fruit-body the volume, and therefore, the weight, of the cap is increased eight times, but the cross-section of the stipe bearing this weight is merely quadrupled (Fig. 75). Adjustment in form with change of size are, therefore, to be expected, otherwise the larger sporophores would have stipes too thin and smaller ones stipes unnecessarily thick for the proper support of the pileus. This is the well known principle of similitude.

Agaric toadstools vary considerably in size from minute species of *Marasmius* to giant species like the horse mushroom (*Agaricus arvensis*). An analysis of agarics with central stipes using the data in the Handbook of the Larger British Fungi (Ramsbottom, 1923) showed quite clearly the expected tendency for form to vary with size (Ingold, 1946). The data given in that book are, however, merely a taxonomist's subjective estimates of fruit-body dimensions. More recently a further analysis (Bond, 1952) has been made based on the illustrations in *Flora Agaricina Danica* (Lange, 1946) each of which is an accurate drawing of an actual representative specimen. The cap diameter and the width of the stipe near its middle were measured for nearly a thousand species. The average cap diameters of all the figured specimens for each width-class of stipe (i.e. 0–1 mm, 1–2 mm ... &c.) were determined and plotted

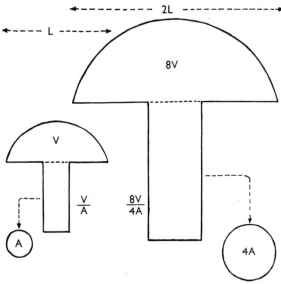

FIG. 75. Two toadstool-like objects, of identical form, but one with double the linear dimensions of the other. In the larger the ratio of cap volume to cross section of stipe has doubled.

against stipe diameter. It is quite clear that the diameter of the pileus does not vary directly as the width of the stipe, but rather that its cube tends to vary as the square of the stipe diameter, as expected on the principle of similitude. This relationship holds not only when all agarics are taken into account, but also when a single large genus such as *Cortinarius* is considered (Fig. 76).

Form in toadstools thus shows a tendency to vary in relation to size. Large agarics have relatively stout, and small ones relatively slender, stalks. In general the stipe is of adequate

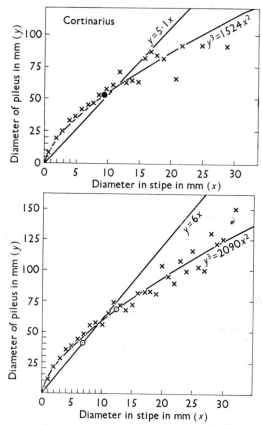

FIG. 76. In both graphs the crosses present diameters of pileus averaged for each stipe diameter (0–1 mm, 1–2 mm, ... etc.), The straight line would be produced if stipe width were proportional to pileus width. The curve is obtained if the cube of the pileus diameter varies as the square of stipe width. Upper graph based on species of *Cortinarius*, lower on all agarics with central stipes. After Bond (1952).

width not only to support the cap, but also to hold it rigidly in a position suitable for spore liberation.

It may be appropriate at this point to consider another feature of fruit-body geometry and, indeed, the rather geometrical form of most sporophores invites considerations of this kind. It has been seen that the gills of an agaric must be a certain minimum distance, which may be called the 'safe distance', apart determined by the range of the basidium as a spore-gun plus a necessary margin of safety probably related to the rigidity of the fruit-body.

If an agaric is examined upside down, it will be seen that the gills converge radially from the circumference towards the stipe. Only rarely are they all of the same length and stretch the whole distance, although this is the condition in most species of *Russula*. In an agaric it might be considered that near the stipe the gills would be the 'safe distance' apart. If this is so then near the circumference of the cap they would be much further apart than necessary for effective spore escape, so shorter gills could be intercalated between the longer ones. Buller (1909) pointed out that there tends to be a series of gills of decreasing size expressed by x,x, $2x$, $4x$ . . . etc., where x is the number of full-length gills.

As we have seen two adjacent gills at their closest approach to the stipe may be considered as being the 'safe distance' apart. Followed outwards towards the periphery of the pileus they become more widely spaced. However, a shorter gill cannot be introduced until the distance apart of the long ones is double the 'safe distance' and only then if its thickness is negligible. From the diagram in Fig. 77 it can be seen, therefore, that as a method of partitioning the under surface of the pileus radial gills seem wasteful. It is clear that the available space could be more efficiently used, indeed increased two and a half times, if cross-partitions the 'safe distance' apart were introduced. This arrangement is well on the way to the polypore condition. On one quadrant of the diagram the space has been filled, experimentally not mathematically, by circular pores with the same diameter as the 'safe distance'. Here the extent of the hymenium is almost doubled.

From the foregoing considerations it seems that the polypore arrangement is more efficient in utilizing the area below the cap than a system of gills. An evolutionary pressure from gills towards pores might, therefore, be expected if the production of the maximum number of spores for the minimum expenditure of fungal tissue has selective advantage. It should, however, be observed that in passing from gills to pores the possibility of the fine readjustment of the hymenial surfaces to the vertical position is lost.

If there really is this supposed advantage, it might be expected that the step from agaric to polypore would have been taken more than once in the course of evolution.

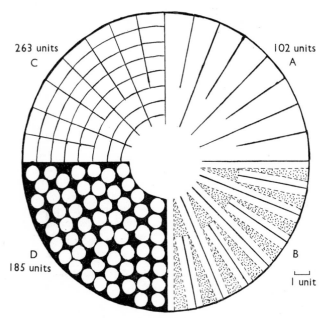

Fig. 77. Diagram of the various ways (A, C, and D) in which the under surface of a toadstool might be partitioned for hymenial surfaces. In B the dotted regions show the 'wasted' areas when partitioning is by radial gills. For each type of partitioning the number of hymenial units available is indicated.

Largely thanks to the work of the modern French mycologists it has become clear that Fries' families Agaricaceae and Polyporaceae cannot be regarded as 'natural' assemblages of fungi. A number of series of what seem to be closely related fungi have been recognized, with agarics at one end, fully developed polypores at the other, and in between intermediate

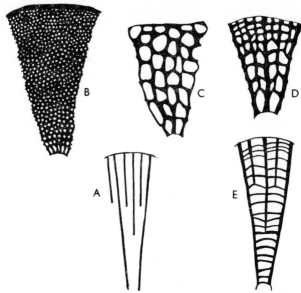

FIG. 78. Sectors of under surface of cap in a number of fungi closely related to *Mycena* (the condition in that genus being shown diagrammatically in A). B. *Mycenoporella clypeata;* C, *Poromycena manipularis;* D, *Phlebomycena madecassensis;* E, *Phaeomycena aureophylla*. B, C, D, and E after Heim (1948).

types having anastomosing gills (Fig. 78). Two series are especially well documented (Heim, 1948):

Mycena, Phaeomycena, Mycenoporella

and

Paxillus, Phylloporus, Boletus

In any such series the question arises: in what direction should it be read? On the whole it is easier to picture the polypore habit developing from the agaric than the reverse, and if indeed there is greater efficiency in the polypore arrangement, this should argue for selection in that direction. But it must not be assumed that the polypore has always arisen from agaric ancestors. Indeed, it is highly probable that the shallow-pored forms have developed directly from thelephoroid types.

We may now return to the question of the trajectories of

discharge and the escape of spores from the pileus. The hymenial surfaces in toadstools and in the shelf or bracket fungi are for the most part vertical or horizontal and downward-facing or at some angle between these two positions. Only rarely does an hymenium face upwards. This is very understandable since basidiospores shot vertically to a height of only a fraction of a millimetre would not be likely to penetrate the laminar layer of air close to the surface, and so would stand little chance of dispersal. Generally speaking an hymenomycete sporophore drops its spores into the potentially turbulent air, whereas the apothecium of an ascomycete, by virtue of the longer range of its spore guns, can with advantage face upwards, since it can shoot its spores through the laminar layer into the tubulent regions above (Fig. 74). Furthermore it must be noted that the position of the hymenium in these two types of fungi is also related to shelter from rain. The hymenium of an hymenomycete is ruined, at least temporarily, by rain whilst that of a cup-fungus, such as *Peziza*, is little affected by wetting. Perhaps because it is too obviously like an umbrella, the importance of a toadstool as a device sheltering the basidia from rain has tended to be overlooked.

In most gill-bearing toadstools the hymenial surfaces are not quite vertical, but the angle to the horizontal slightly exceeds 90°. This is because the gill is normally wedge-shaped in section narrowing towards its free edge, and this no doubt has some value in the escape of falling spores.

In a number of hymenomycete sporophores where the gills are very closely packed or where the hymenial tubes are particularly narrow, the question of how the spores manage to escape so efficiently raises certain problems. These are particularly acute in the perennial polypores such as *Ganoderma applanatum*. In that species the distance of basidiospore discharge is 0·05–0·1 mm. The hymenial tubes are 0·1–0·2 mm in diameter and in a two-year old specimen these may be several centimetres long and lined throughout with active basidia. The tubes are accurately positioned by their positively geotropic growth and this, combined with the great rigidity of the fruit-body and its broad attachment to a tree-trunk, ensures that the tubes remain perfectly vertical (Fig. 79). Even so there seems to be no margin of safety and it is difficult to understand how the spores manage their free fall without a considerable percentage becoming stranded on the walls of the tubes. Nevertheless, microscopic examination indicates that few if any spores experience this fate.

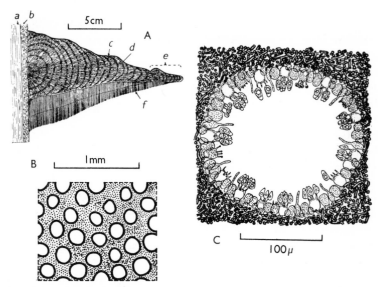

FIG. 79. *Ganoderma applanatum*. A, vertical section of a small fruit-body growing on an ash tree: *a*, wood; *b*, bark, *c*, upper 'crust' of fungus; *d*, zoned fibrous pileus tissue formed in first year; *e*, additional pileus tissue produced in second year; *f*, hymenial tubes (the dotted line indicates the boundary between the tubes formed in the first year (above) and in the second (below)). B, horizontal section of fruit-body at level of the hymenial tubes. The thick black line around each pore is the hymenium. C, details of a single hymenial pore.

It has been suggested that static electric charges on the spores may be involved in keeping them in midstream during their fall down narrow hymenial tubes. Long ago Buller (1909) drew attention to the fact that spores in air are habitually charged, and this was confirmed by Gregory (1957) for the escaping basidiospores of *Ganoderma* which were shown mostly to carry a positive charge. Further work (Swinbank *et al.*, 1964) with *Merulius lacrymans*, in which the average magnitude of the charge on the spores was determined, has indicated that this is so small that it could have no appreciable effect in deflecting spores moving under the influence of gravity. Again if any deflection is to occur from this cause, a repelling charge of the same sign would be required on the hymenium, and there is no evidence of this.

The effect of slight tilting on the escape of spores from individual hymenial tubes in *Polyporus betulinus* has been studied (Taggart, 1964). Taggart found that the result of tilting is to reduce escape to the extent that would be expected from purely geometrical considerations assuming straight vertical fall of basidiospores, and this in itself is strong evidence that the spores fall in this way. However, the basidiospores of *P. betulinus* are elongated ($5 \cdot 5 \times 2 \ \mu$) and if they were to fall with random orientation in still unimpeded air, their average angle of descent would be several degrees from the vertical (Fig. 73) and a high proportion would fail to escape from the hymenial tubes. This again poses the problem of how such spores become oriented in the narrow confines of the hymenial tube. It would seem likely that frictional drag associated with the air in contact with the hymenial surface might tend to tilt the spores into a vertical position with the result that they would be brought into a position to fall vertically as in Yarwood and Hazen's narrow-tube experiment (see p. 128).

Although details of the trajectories of spores in the intergill spaces and within hymenial tubes need further study, there seems no doubt that an essential feature for the escape of spores is that the air in these regions should be still, even when outside it is turbulent. This state of affairs is probably fairly well established in an agaric with deep, crowded gills, but reaches its extreme expression in a bracket fungus such as *Ganoderma applanatum* with long and narrow tubes. A further necessary consequence of this stillness of the air is its saturation with water vapour; it has already been suggested that for continued basidiospore discharge this is essential.

For an understanding of function in toadstools and bracket fungi it is necessary to consider form and structure, but contemplative morphology and assumption of function from form is dangerous, unless supported by experimental study. Perhaps the apparent dispersal story in a hymenomycete is not always the true one and, for example, the suggestion of Talbot (1952) that small invertebrates may play a significant part should not be ignored.

REFERENCES

BOND, T. E. T. (1952). A further note on size and form in agarics. *Trans. Br. mycol. Soc.* **35**, 190–194.

BULLER, A. H. R. (1909, 1922, 1924, 1931). *Researches on fungi* Vols. I–IV. London.

DERX, H. G. (1948). *Itersonilia*, nouveau genre de sporobolomycètes à mycélium bouclé. *Bull. bot. Gdns. Buitenz.* Ser. III, **18**, 465–472.

GREGORY, P. H. (1957). Electrostatic charges on spores of fungi in air *Nature, Lond.* **180**, 330.

——(1961) *The microbiology of the atmosphere.* London.

HEIM, R. (1948). Phylogeny and natural classification of macro-fungi. *Trans. Br. mycol. Soc.* **30**, 161–178.

INGOLD, C. T. (1939). *Spore discharge in land plants.* Oxford.

—— (1946). Size and form in agarics. *Trans. Br. mycol. Soc.* **29**, 108–113.

LANGE, J. E. (1946). *Flora Agaricina Danica.* Copenhagen.

LARGE, E. C. (1961). Pursuits of mycology, *Trans. Br. mycol. Soc.* **44**, 1–23.

MARTIN, G. W. (1925). Morphology of *Conidiobolus villosus. Bot. Gaz.* **80**, 311–318.

MÜLLER, D. (1954). Die Abschleuderung der Sporen von *Sporobolomyces*—Spiegelhefe—gefilmt. *Friesia* **5**, 65–74.

OLIVE, L. S. (1964). Spore discharge mechanism in Basidiomycetes. *Science* **146**, 542–3.

PLUNKETT, B. E. (1961). The change of tropism in *Polyporus brumalis* stipes and the effect of directional stimuli on pileus differentiation. *Ann. Bot.* **25**, 206–223.

PRINCE, A. E. (1943). Basidium formation and spore discharge in *Gymnosporangium nidus-avis. Farlowia* **1**, 79–93.

RAMSBOTTOM, J. (1923). *A handbook of the larger British fungi.* London.

SWINBANK, P., TAGGART, J. and HUTCHINSON, S. A. (1964). The measurement of electrostatic charges on spores of *Merulius lacrymans* (Wulf.) Fr. *Ann. Bot.* **28**, 239–249.

TALBOT, P. H. B. (1952). Dispersal of fungus spores by small animals inhabiting wood and bark. *Trans. Br. mycol. Soc.* **35**, 123–128.

TAGGART, J. (1961). Sporulation in fungi with special reference to Hymenomycetes. Ph.D. thesis, Univ. Glasgow.

WESTON, W. H. (1923). Production and dispersal of conidia in the Philippine *Sclerosporas* of maize. *J. agric. Res.* **23**, 239–278.

YARWOOD, C. E. and HAZEN, W. E. (1942). Vertical orientation of powdery mildew conidia during fall. *Science* **96**, 316–317.

VII

GASTEROMYCETES, OR NATURE TRIES AGAIN

BASIDIOMYCETES constitute one of the great classes of Fungi with about 600 genera and 14000 species. Rusts (Uredineae) and smuts (Ustilaginales) together contribute about 160 genera and 5300 species, and gelatinous fungi (Tremellales) some 65 genera and 500 species. However, the largest division of Basidiomycetes is Hymenomycetes with 275 genera and 7000 species. Finally, in Gasteromycetes there are about 110 genera and 700 species (Ainsworth, 1961). Thus *species* of Hymenomycetes outnumber Gasteromycetes in the world flora by about ten to one, but there is less disparity in the number of *genera* in the two groups. The greater generic diversity may, perhaps, be associated with Gasteromycetes being at a highly experimental stage in their evolution.

Considering the differences between Hymenomycetes and Gasteromycetes, the essential feature is that in Hymenomycetes the basidia are displayed on hymenial surfaces which are so disposed that when they discharge their spores these fall freely from the sporophore. In Gasteromycetes, however, when the basidia are mature the hymenial surfaces, which are often poorly defined, are not exposed and the individual spores are not violently discharged. Apparently correlated with this the basidiospore is not poised asymmetrically on a curved tapering sterigma, but is either arranged symmetrically on a sterigma which rarely tapers, or is sessile (Fig. 80). At maturity in most Gasteromycetes the basidium breaks down and the spores lie freely within the ripe sporophore.

The classification used in this chapter is that given by Ainsworth (1961). In this Gasteromycetes are subdivided into a number of orders: Hymenogastrales, Phallales, Lycoperdales, Sclerodermatales, and Nidulariales. Hymenogastrales include

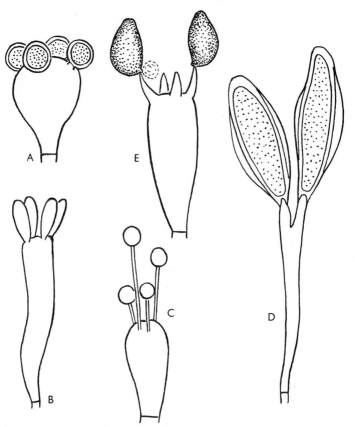

FIG. 80. Gasteromycete basidia of *Scleroderma aurantium* (A), *Phallus impudicus* (B), *Lycoperdon perlatum* (C), and *Hymenogaster citrinus* (D). Also the basidium of the hymenomycete *Panaeolus campanulatus* (E) showing two spores still attached one of which is on the point of discharge. All highly magnified.

several families especially Secotiaceae, and Hymenogastraceae a family of specialized hypogeal fungi.

Although for convenience most mycologists retain the nineteenth century concept of Gasteromycetes, it has become increasingly evident that this taxon cannot reasonably be regarded as a natural one. Largely due to the work of Heim,

Malençon, and Romagnesi in France, and of the American mycologists Singer and Smith, a number of suggestive series have been identified which seem to link gasteromycete genera with others amongst Hymenomycetes. In seeking these links most reliance has been placed on characters which do not appear to have adaptive significance such as shape, colour and ornamentation of spores, and the details of hyphal construction of the fruit-body.

Certain genera of Gasteromycetes are unmistakably linked with toadstools. A striking example is the genus *Secotium* with some 25 species. *S. agaricoides* in its early development agrees exactly with *Agaricus*. However, the gills anastomose considerably and the fruit-body does not open to expose hymenial surfaces from which spores are shot. Instead, at maturity the spores are set free passively within the sporophore and most of the gill tissue breaks down. Eventually the fruit-body cracks in rather a rough and irregular manner and the dry spores sift out (Buller, 1922).

On the basis of the peculiar 'crystallographic' spores combined with their pink colour Romagnesi (1933) sees a clear connexion between the agaric genus *Rhodophyllus* and the hypogeous gasteromycete *Richoniella*.

Having regard to details of histology especially the presence of lactiferous hyphae and nests of sphaerocysts combined with amyloid spores, Heim (1948) and Singer and Smith (1960) see a clear connexion between toadstools of the *Lactarius-Russula* type and such secotiaceous genera as *Elasmomyces* and *Archangiella*.

Other plausible connexions are between the ink-cap *Coprinus* and the black-spored gasteromycete *Gyrophragmium*, between *Galera* in agarics and *Podaxis* in Gasteromycetes both with the same type of brown spore having a large terminal germ pore, and between *Boletus* and *Rhizopogon*, both attacked by the same rather specialized mould, *Sepedonium chrysospermum*.

There are thus half a dozen distinct and fairly convincing connecting series between Gasteromycetes and fleshy Hymenomycetes. However, it is worth noting that all these connexions are with the secotiaceous types within Hymenogastrales, only one of the five orders of Gasteromycetes. Good evidence of links between the remaining four orders and Hymenomycetes is non-existent, nor are there any obvious lines joining Hymenogastrales with other Gasteromycetes. From the point of view of a *natural* classification it might be best to shunt the order Hymenogastrales from Gasteromycetes and couple it on to Hymenomycetes with a necessary re-definition of the characteristics of that group. However, most mycologists will probably, for a long time to come, want to retain the traditional grouping into Hymenomycetes, as at present defined, and Gasteromycetes, and be content to recognize that these are essentially *biological* rather than *natural* taxa.

Assuming the validity of the connecting lines between Hymenomycetes and Hymenogastrales, there remains the recurrent question in a case of this kind of the direction evolution has taken. There are differing views, and some eminent taxonomists support the thesis that Hymenomycetes have been derived from gasteromycete ancestors (Singer and Smith, 1960). If this is correct the evidence would suggest that several separate lines must have been involved and, therefore, the basidium as a spore gun must have developed again and again from non-explosive basidia. This seems extremely difficult to envisage. It is much easier to imagine that the types of basidia found in Gasteromycetes have arisen by degeneration from hymenomycete ancestors. In an almost complete absence of a fossil record, anything like certainty is impossible in dealing with the phylogeny of fungi, but the view is adopted here that Gasteromycetes have, in all probability, been derived from hymenomycete stock.

Having lost the delicate hymenomycete equipment of spore liberation, it seems that Gasteromycetes have been forced to develop methods of dispersal along new and original lines. Nature has tried again. Gasteromycetes may best be understood as a remarkable series of experiments in spore liberation.

It may be legitimate to speculate on the possible causes of this retreat from the hymenomycete condition and, perhaps, the answer is an ecological one. Generally speaking Hymenomycetes are little adapted to xerophytic conditions. The great

144

majority of fleshy fungi are very sensitive to dryness. Even those leathery lignicolous forms capable of enduring drought can, with few exceptions, continue to liberate spores only under humid conditions. On the other hand Gasteromycetes reach their fullest development in warm, dry parts of the world and mostly the spore dispersal mechanisms do not show such dependence on continual dampness of the air.

There are five major kinds of dispersal in Gasteromycetes: dry-spore types dispersed by wind, slime-spore fungi spread by insects, hypogeal forms relying on rodents for dispersal, splash-cup fungi, and the catapult of *Sphaerobolus*.

The most familiar dry-spore mechanism is to be found in species of the puff-ball *Lycoperdon* (Fig. 81). At maturity the fertile region, or gleba, is converted into a capillitium of dry springy hyphae, derived from the trama, saturated, as a powder-puff is loaded with powder, with dry spores. In *L. perlatum* the capillitium consists of long, thick-walled, almost wirey, threads about 8 μ wide but often over a centimetre long and very sparingly branched, or even unbranched. One group of these forms a central basal tuft in the capsule; the remainder radiating inwards from the peridial wall. This is thin, papery, and unwettable. Eventually, the capsule opens by an apical ostiole. Wind blowing across this may suck out spores, but essentially the whole structure seems to be a bellows mechanism operated by falling water-drops (Gregory, 1949). Large drops several millimetres in diameter are involved from heavy showers of rain or dripping from trees. A drop striking the unwettable peridium momentarily depresses it, and a cloud of spores escapes through the ostiole, the capsule at once resuming its normal form due to the resilience of the capillitium within.

The same mechanism operates in the earth-stars, for example in *Geastrum triplex*. The young onion-shaped sporophore is buried in the litter of beech leaves with only its pointed end reaching the surface. The three-layered exoperidium, of which the innermost layer is fleshy, splits along several lines of weakness extending from the apex towards the base thus carving out the 'rays' of the star which eventually bend backwards

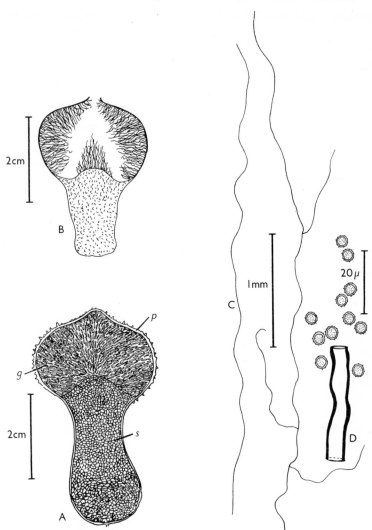

FIG. 81. *Lycoperdon perlatum.* A, fully grown sporophore in longitudinal section showing stipe (*s*), peridium (*p*) and gleba (*g*) in which there are numerous elongated chambers lined by hymenium. B, mature dry specimen in longitudinal section; the capillitium threads are shown but the spores are omitted. C, individual capillitium threads. D, part of a capillitium thread and some spores.

pushing aside the leaf litter and exposing the capsule with its thin wall of papery endoperidium. These rays may bend so far that they raise the capsule significantly and break all connection with the parent mycelium in the soil. The capsule itself opens by an apical ostiole, which is a much more specialized structure than in *Lycoperdon*. Within are unbranched capillitial threads, bound together in fine sheaves, radiating outwards from a conspicuous columella and inwards from the endoperidium (Fig. 82).

It is interesting to observe an area where *G. triplex* occurs during a downpour of rain. Being of much the same colour as the beech leaves amongst which they grow, the sporophores are sometimes difficult to locate, but if the rain is heavy they are at once betrayed by the easily visible puffs of spores arising from them.

It seems that species of the genus *Tylostoma*, although taxonomically rather remote from both *Lycoperdon* and *Geastrum*, behave in just the same way. *Tylostoma* spp. are, however, essentially desert fungi and the puffing mechanism may be operated by wind-blown sand more often than by raindrops.

Bovista plumbea, a common British pasture species, is very much like a puff-ball (Fig. 83). The exoperidium breaks down to a greater or lesser extent leaving the papery endoperidium as the essential capsule wall. The ripe sporophore has a definite apical mouth through which puffs of spores may escape under the action of bombarding raindrops. The capillitium is, however, very different from that of *Lycoperdon*. It consists of a mass of separate units, each a three-dimensional system of branched, stiff hyphae diverging from a central point, and each about 1 mm across. The whole mass of these tiny units saturated with the dry, tailed basidiospores, characteristic of *Bovista*, forms a powder-puff as effective as that of *Lycoperdon* or *Geastrum*. Often the sporophore, surrounded solely by the endoperidium, breaks free and, being very light, is easily trundled by the wind scattering spores as it bounces along without any need of rain to activate its bellows mechanism.

The giant puff-balls, included in the genus *Calvatia*, do not have the bellows mechanism of spore liberation. Thus when

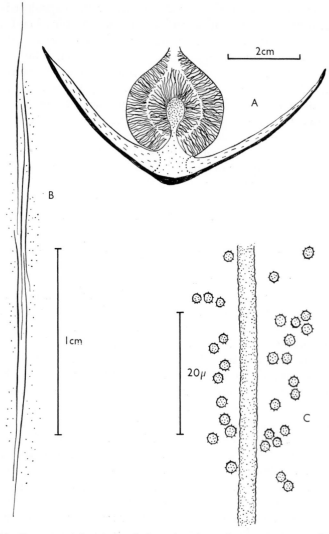

FIG. 82. *Geastrum triplex*. A, vertical section through a mature sporophore showing sheafs of capillitium threads attached to the columella and to the inner peridium (capsule wall). B, single sheaf of capillitium threads (some-what separated) with some associated spores. C, part of a capillitium thread with some spores.

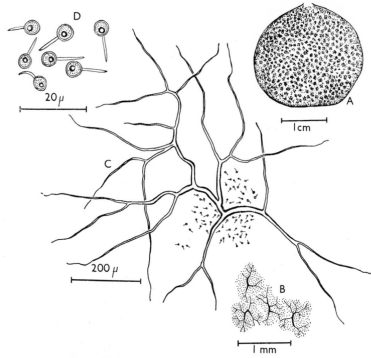

FIG. 83. *Bovista plumbea.* A, Loose capsule surrounded only by papery inner peridium and containing 'crumbs' of dry gleba. B, four 'crumbs' each with a skeleton consisting of a capillitium element. C, single capillitium element and a very few associated spores. D, seven spores.

fully mature the sporophore of *Calvatia caelata* (Fig. 84) opens widely to expose a great mass of very dry powdery spores kept loose and uncompacted by a branched system of capillitium threads. Spores are freely blown away by wind. Further as spores are removed from the exposed surface of the spore mass, the capillitium, which is extremely brittle, is also blown away and thus does not interfere with the liberation of deeper layers of spores.

A very remarkable dry-spore mechanism is found in *Podaxis.* This fungus is of widespread occurrence in warmer countries. The taxonomy of the genus is in a confused state. It has been

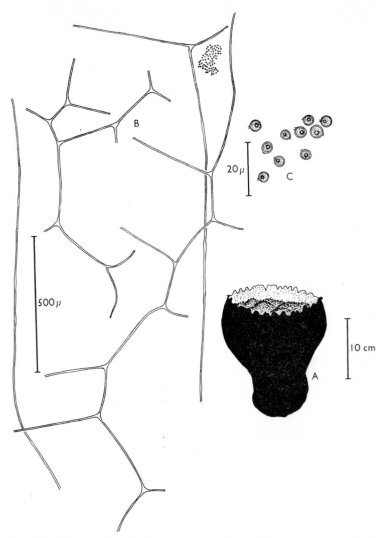

Fig. 84. *Calvatia caelata*. A, dry open sporophore with spore mass exposed. B, capillitium threads and a few spores; most of the tips represent naturally broken ends. C, spores.

suggested that only a single, rather polymorphic species is involved, but it seems unlikely that this is the true position. In Ghana, the region in which *Podaxis* is known to the writer, there are two clearly defined species. The discussion below is based on the taller species with a narrower cap and smaller spores which grows associated with large termite nests. For this the name *P. pistillaris* is provisionally used. *Podaxis*, having a distinct stipe and cap, has a resemblance to certain agarics (Fig. 85). In general form it shows a striking agreement with the ink-cap *Coprinus comatus* as that fungus appears at the start of spore liberation. However, the texture is entirely different. The stipe of *Podaxis* is firm, rigid, and almost woody, and the cap tissue forms a dry leathery peridium. The gleba is developed between the stipe, in the cap region, and the peridium. At maturity this gleba becomes a mass of dark brown powdery spores penetrated by very numerous coiled capillitium threads which arise from the stipe and pass outwards to meet the peridium without actually being attached to it. These capillitium strands are often 2–3 cm long, completely unbranched and apparently non-septate. Some of them undergo a spiral splitting giving almost the impression of spirally thickened elaters. When the sporophore is fully ripe the peridium separates slightly from the stipe at the base of the cap and spores sift slowly out. This can happen under the influence of wind and probably also in heavy rain.

Sreeramulu and Seshavataram (1962) working in India have found that spores of *Podaxis* contribute an abundant element to the air spora there. The mean diurnal periodicity curve showed a very definite maximum around midnight. What determines this is by no means clear but rainfall does not seem to be involved.

Another interesting genus of dry-spore Gasteromycetes is *Battarraea*. The best-known species is *B. phalloides*, but even that would seem to be rare. A large species is illustrated in Fig. 86. The mature, expanded fruit-body consists of a dome-like cap borne on a tall and very stiff stalk arising from within a cup-like volva. The ripe glebal mass is at first covered by a thin endoperidium but this ruptures in a rather irregular manner

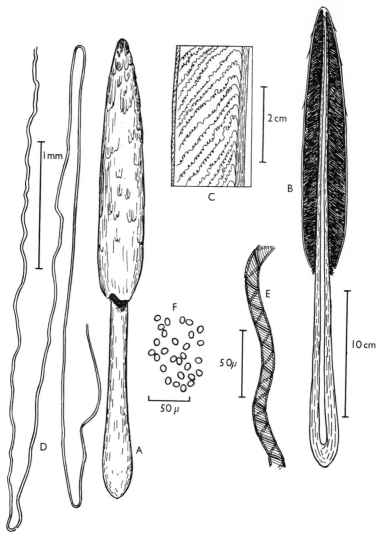

FIG. 85. *Podaxis pistillaris*. A, mature sporophore. B, same in longitudinal section; spore-mass black. C, small part of B more highly magnified to show attachment of the unbranched capillitium threads to the stipe and their extension almost to the peridium; spores omitted. D, part of a capillitium thread bent at three points to fit page. E, smaller part of D more highly magnified. F, spores.

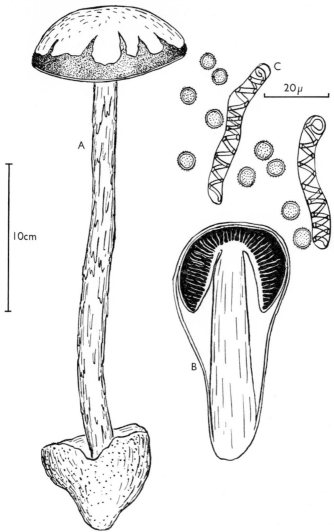

FIG. 86. *Battarrea sp.* (Drawn from specimens in B.M. (Nat. Hist.) London collected in Cyprus). A, sporophore with woody stipe arising from buried volva; inner peridium peeling off to expose the gleba. B, longitudinal section of a younger specimen; coarse stiff hyphal strands (white) extend outwards through the gleba (black). C, spores and elaters from the ripe gleba.

exposing a dry spore-mass held amongst rather stiff capillitium strands. The chief interest from the point of view of dispersal is that intermixed with the spores are much elongated cells with spiral thickening showing a striking resemblance to the elaters of liverworts. Whether by violent movements on drying they play any part in the active liberation of spores is unknown.

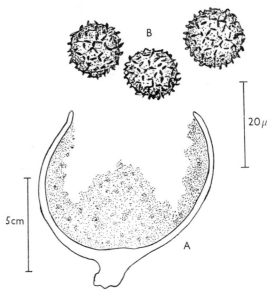

FIG. 87. *Scleroderma aurantium.* A, longitudinal section of a mature opened sporophore containing the earthy spore-mass (gleba). B, individual spores.

When elaters from a museum specimen were allowed to absorb water and then watched during drying no vigorous movements were observed, but this may not have given a true indication of what happens in fresh material.

A very familiar example of a dry-spore gasteromycete is the earth-ball, *Scleroderma aurantium* (Fig. 87). In this the gleba at maturity becomes a dry, earthy mass of spores not permeated by a significant capillitium. The thickish peridium ruptures in an irregular manner freely exposing the rather large spores which, apparently, are blown away by wind. As a spore-liberating mechanism the earth-ball seems crude indeed by comparison with *Lycoperdon* and *Geastrum*. Nevertheless, dispersal in this fungus seems to be highly effective since it is one of the commonest British species found in great numbers on sandy soil on heaths and in woods.

We may now pass to another family of Gasteromycetes: Hymenogastraceae. These are essentially subterranean fungi. Quite a number of the higher fungi have, as it were, gone to earth. Truffles, probably derived from ancestors of the cup-fungus type, are familiar examples. Indeed, within the great group of Ascomycetes comparative studies of structure and development strongly suggest that the hypogeal habit has been evolved along several distinct lines of descent. In the same way in Gasteromycetes hypogeal forms have apparently arisen and, as in Ascomycetes, the evidence indicates a number of independent evolutionary lines. The family Hymenogastraceae is probably best regarded not as a natural taxon, but as one consisting of elements of the same biological type.

It would appear that the hypogeal fungi generally have the same dispersal story. Sporophores when ripe give out a smell detectable by rodents which grub up and eat them. The spores pass through the alimentary canal and are deposited unharmed in the dung. It has to be admitted, however, that this story is largely based on inference, and there is very little observational or experimental basis for it. Studies on the essential dispersal story of the hypogeal fungi would be very welcome.

One sharply characterized order of Gasteromycetes, Phallales, has fruit-bodies obviously related to insect dispersal of spores. There are some 20 genera and their richest development is in Australasia and tropical countries.

The sub-mature fruit body is like a soft egg (Fig. 88) formed just below the soil or leaf-litter level at the end of a rhizomorph traceable back to buried wood. Finally in most genera a spongy stalk within the 'egg' elongates with remarkable speed carrying the slimy spore-mass above the ground to a height of several inches. In *Clathrus* and its allies there is no stalk, but the spore-slime coats a more or less spherical open network which quickly expands soon after the 'egg' ruptures.

In all species the exposed spore-slime contains abundant

sugar and emits a strong and unpleasant odour. The basidio-spores themselves are minute and smooth-walled. This is a type of spore encountered repeatedly in fungi where insect dispersal is the rule.

It is of some interest to compare the two commonest British phalloids: *Phallus impudicus* (Stinkhorn) and *Mutinus caninus*

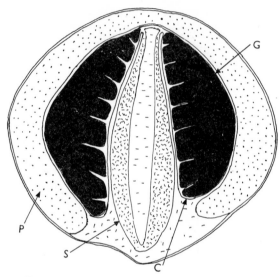

FIG. 88. *Phallus impudicus.* Fully grown 'egg' in longitudinal section. P, gelatinous middle peridium; S, stipe; C, cap; G, gleba. Natural size.

(Dog's Stinkhorn). *P. impudicus* has a strong odour detectable at a distance of many yards, but *M. caninus* has to be held quite close to be smelt. Stinkhorns usually expand from the 'eggs' in the forenoon. In *P. impudicus* the cap is seen crowded with flies and bluebottles, and by evening it is normally left white and spore-free (Fig. 89). On the other hand in *Mutinus* flies are not very often seen eating the slime and very frequently collapsed specimens can be collected with the spore-load undiminished. It is tempting to suggest that this difference in these two stinkhorns is connected with the difference in the intensity of their smell.

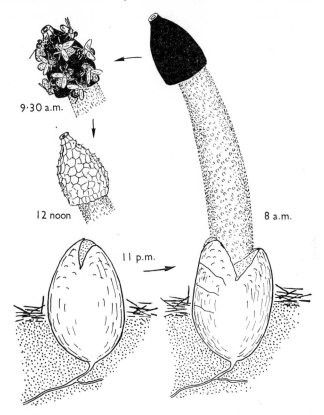

9·30 a.m.

12 noon

8 a.m.

11 p.m.

Fig. 89. *Phallus impudicus*. At 11 p.m. the young fruit-body is at 'egg' stage and the outer papery layer of the peridium has torn exposing the jelly of the middle peridium. Next morning at 8 a.m. the stipe has elongated carrying up the cap with the spore-slime and leaving the peridium as a volva around the base. By 9.30 a.m. the slime is giving out a strong smell and has attracted flies; by noon all the spore-slime has been removed.

It is natural to try and interpret the structure of phalloids in terms of possible importance in dispersal. What may be the biological significance of the remarkable network crinoline of *Dictyophora* (Fig. 90) is by no means clear, but the scarlet sterile rays of *Aseroë* (Fig. 90), surrounding the central mass of spore-slime, are very suggestive of the brilliant petals of an entomophilous flower, and there is little doubt that they have the same function.

The dispersal story in Phallales is somewhat unsatisfactory because of lack of knowledge of the fate of the spores. Germination has not yet been observed. Spores which have passed through the alimentary tract of flies appear quite unaltered,

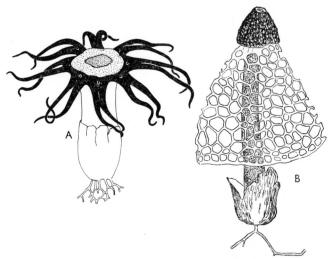

FIG. 90. A, *Aseroë rubra:* the central stippled area is the spore-containing slime, the bifid sterile rays are crimson; after Massee. B, *Dictyophora indusiata*: sporophore showing the net-like 'crinoline' below the cap with its spore-slime; for simplicity only the front half of the 'crinoline' is shown.

but, as with those taken directly from the sporiferous slime, they fail to germinate under laboratory conditions. Indeed, in general gasteromycete spores are difficult to germinate (Bulmer and Beneke, 1964). It would, however, seem unlikely that the spores of stinkhorns are no longer capable of germination. The probability is that the conditions in nature which induce germination have not yet been identified. *Phallus impudicus* is a very common species with a considerable geographic range. Its mechanism of dispersal may, therefore, be assumed to be efficient and there does not seem to be any subsidiary means of spread apart from the basidiospores.

Perhaps the most extraordinary specialization in connexion with dispersal is to be seen in Nidulariales, but the mechanisms in its two families, Nidulariaceae and Sphaerobolaceae, are so different that they must be considered separately.

The family Nidulariaceae embraces a number of genera in all of which the sporophore contains within it a small number of hard, almost seed-like, packets of spores known as peridiola. The sporophore opens at maturity to expose the peridiola which are liberated for the most part by rain-splash. The significance of the form of the fruit-body was appreciated by Buller near the end of his life, and the story was later developed in detail by Brodie (1951, 1956) who recognized a series: *Nidularia, Nidula, Crucibulum,* and *Cyathus* in order of increasing splash-cup efficiency.

Cyathus striatus (Fig. 91) is a fairly common and widely distributed species found usually on rotting wood. It was illustrated beautifully by the Tulasne brothers over a hundred years ago and Brodie has maintained their traditions in his fine drawings of structure in relation to function in this species.

When the sporophore is fully mature it is an open vase about 1·5 cm high with a circular mouth roughly 1 cm across. It is firmly emplaced on the woody substratum and contains a dozen or so peridiola, each a hard seed-like structure, discoid and 2–3 mm in diameter. In section the peridiolum is seen to have a wall of several layers, including a very hard one, and there is a central flattened cavity lined by hymenium. However, at maturity the basidia are disorganized and the centre is filled with a mass of spores. Each peridiolum is attached by a short stalk, 2–3 mm long, to the inner wall of the peridial vase. The stalk is clearly differentiated into a lower part (sheath) and an upper part (purse). The purse is a delicate, hollow, tubular structure closed below, and coiled up within is a rope of hyphae (funiculus) associated like the strands of a wire cable. The upper end of this is firmly attached to the peridiolum, but the lower, free end is frayed out to form the hapteron, a mass of very sticky hyphae. The purse is connected with the sheath by a sheaf of hyphae forming the 'middle piece'. This can be demonstrated if a peridiolum is carefully pulled away from its attachment.

A large drop of water falling into the open sporophore is broken up and reflected from the splash-cup as a number of

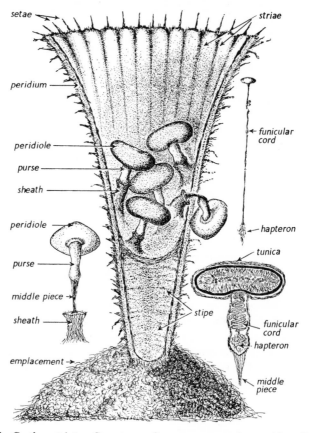

FIG. 91. *Cyathus striatus.* Structure of mature sporophore. After Brodie (1951).

separate droplets some of which may carry peridiola to a distance of a metre or two. Under the impact of the drop the peridiolum with its attached funiculus breaks free from its stalk by rupture of the purse, and when this happens the hyphae of the hapteron spread out almost explosively. Probably the funiculus is still coiled in the reflected droplet as it travels through the air. If the droplet strikes such an object as a fine stem, the hapteron adheres strongly and, although the peridiolum may be carried further by its momentum and the funiculus be stretched to a length of 5–10 cm, the peridiolum is finally arrested by its efficient tether. Sometimes this may lead to the funiculus becoming coiled several times around a narrow stem or the peridiolum may simply be left hanging from such a horizontal object as a leaf.

The subsequent fate of the peridiolum is not known with any certainty. Falling on rotten wood it may germinate directly to produce a dikaryotic mycelium without the contained spores being involved at all. However, it is to be noted that quite a number of Nidulariaceae are coprophilous. For example *Cyathus stercorarius* is a common species on horse or cow dung, or on heavily manured ground. In coprophilous types it may well be that, as with other dung fungi, the peridiola are eaten with the herbage and germination occurs after passing through the alimentary tract. Brodie has, indeed, observed that the spores of *C. stercorarius* germinate best following mild heat treatment such as might be experienced in passage through an animal.

Cyathus striatus seems highly specialized in connexion with splash dispersal. Even the striae lining the vase and the setae around its rim look as if they have significance in connexion with droplet reflection.

As we descend Brodie's suggested series specialization seems to decrease. There is still a well-developed funiculus in *Crucibulum*, but the form of the splash-cup does not appear so perfect as that of *Cyathus*. In *Nidula* the splash-cup is still there but the rather small peridiola are devoid of funiculus. Instead each is sticky over its whole surface. In *Nidularia* the spherical sporophore ruptures in an irregular manner and, although splash dispersal may well occur, the structure can hardly be called a splash-cup.

Sphaerobolus is classified in Sphaerobolaceae, a family usually included in Nidulariales. The taxonomy of the genus is difficult, but probably the majority of collections can be

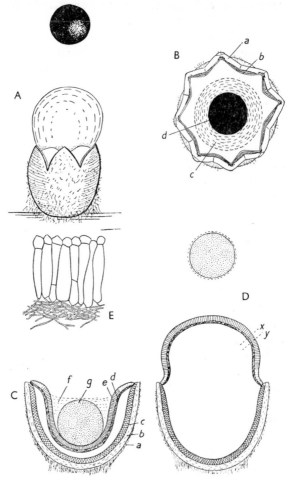

FIG. 92. *Sphaerobolus stellatus*. A, Sporophore at instant of discharge; the inner cup has turned inside out exposing its wet, shining surface. B, looking directly into an opened sporophore before discharge: *a*, outer cup; *b*, inner cup; *c*, lubricating fluid in which the glebal mass (*d*) is submerged. C, vertical section of opened sporophore. *a,b,c*, tissue layers of outer cup; *d* and *e*, tissue layers of inner cup; *f*, lubricating fluid; *g*, glebal mass. D, same at moment of discharge. E, part of inner cup (between lines *x* and *y* in D) highly magnified. A to D × 15.

assign to *S. stellatus*, a common species found in most parts of the world growing on very rotten wood or old dung pads. Further, unlike other Gasteromycetes, it grows and fruits readily in pure culture on a suitable medium such as oatmeal agar, provided the light intensity is sufficient and the temperature is below 25°C. In maintaining the fungus in a fruiting condition it is best to start new cultures from discharged glebal bodies (peridiola).

S. stellatus (Fig. 92) is one of the smallest of Gasteromycetes with a fruit-body only about 2 mm in diameter. From this at maturity a spherical peridiolum, or glebal mass, 1 mm across is catapulted to a distance of several metres. A beautiful detailed account is given by Buller (1933).

The nearly ripe fruit-body is spherical and anchored to the substratum by a cottony mycelium. In vertical section it is seen to consist of a spore-containing gleba surrounded by a peridium of six histologically distinct layers. When mature it splits along a number of lines radiating from the apex, thus carving out four to eight teeth of peridial tissue which bend outwards exposing the spherical glebal mass. At the same time the peridium separates into two cups, one fitting inside the other and each with a toothed margin. The cups remain in contact only at the tips of the teeth. The outer cup is composed of the three outermost layers of the peridium, and the inner cup of two of the remaining layers. The sixth layer, which was in immediate contact with the gleba, has largely autolysed at this stage to produce a fluid, so that the glebal mass fits loosely in the inner cup just submerged by liquid.

Contributing largely to the inner wall of the inner cup is a palisade tissue of relatively big cells, but the outer wall is composed of fine interwoven tangential hyphae. By absorption of water the inner surface of the cup tends to increase. Thus strains are set up which are suddenly and violently released by the inner cup turning inside out, thereby catapulting the glebal mass to a distance of several metres.

Walker and Anderson (1925) pointed out that before the sporophore opens the palisade cells of the peridial layer are rich in glycogen. As in so many structures concerned with violent discharge in fungi, this disappears in the later stages of ripening and is presumably converted to sugar with a consequent increase in osmotic pressure leading to a build-up of turgor. Walker considered that this glycogen was converted to maltose. However, more recent study by Engel and Schneider (1963), using paper chromatography, indicates that glucose is the sugar produced, the amount in the tissues of the inner cup increasing rapidly from the first appearance of stellate splitting of the sporophore until it is wide open and ready to discharge its glebal mass.

The soft sticky glebal mass has a thin, brown wall composed of disorganized peridial cells. It contains very numerous minute spores and a much smaller number of somewhat larger dikaryotic cells or gemmae. On a suitable substratum the glebal mass germinates immediately producing dikaryotic mycelium, apparently derived from the gemmae. The basidiospores tend to remain dormant. However, Walker has succeeded in inducing their germination in water containing a little pepsin.

Sphaerobolus is both a lignicolous and a coprophilous fungus. As pointed out by Buller (1933), it seems to have all the features of specialized coprophilous fungi shown also by *Pilobolus* spp., *Dasyobolus immersus*, and *Podospora* spp.: there is a large and strongly adhesive spore-mass discharged sufficiently far to reach the grass around the dung; the spores are screened from light after discharge; and the spore-gun is aimed by positive phototropism. In *Sphaerobolus* phototropism is associated with the response of the whole sporophore to light, whilst in *Pilobolus* the sporangiophore reacts, in *Podospora* it is the neck of the perithecium, and in *Dasyobolus* the individual projecting asci. It is interesting to note that the nearly spherical unopened fruit-body of *Sphaerobolus* is capable of phototropic reaction as little as two days before it opens (Alasoadura, 1963). However, the opened sporophore has no power of reorientation to light from a new direction. A further parallel between all these specialized coprophilous fungi is their diurnal periodocity of discharge. In nature, spore discharge is almost limited to daytime.

GASTEROMYCETES, OR NATURE TRIES AGAIN

When *Sphaerobolus* occurs on dung there is little doubt that it has found its way there from discharged glebal masses, on grass eaten by the animal, by way of the alimentary canal. Thus it behaves like most of the other members of the coprophilous flora.

The picture here presented of dispersal in Gasteromycetes is, no doubt, incomplete, but nevertheless its essential features are clear enough, namely the extraordinary range of dispersal mechanism, contrasting sharply with the essential uniformity of the spore-liberating equipment in Hymenomycetes.

REFERENCES

AINSWORTH, G. C. 1961. *Ainsworth and Bisby's dictionary of fungi.* London.
ALASOADURA, S. O. 1963. Fruiting in *Sphaerobolus* with special reference to light. *Ann. Bot.* **27**, 125–145.
BRODIE, H. J. 1951. The splash-cup dispersal mechanism in plants. *Canad. J. Bot.* **29**, 224–234.
—— (1956). The structure and function of the funiculus of the Nidulariaceae. *Svensk. bot. Tidskr.* **50**, 142–162.
BULLER, A. H. R. 1922. *Researches on Fungi Vol. II.* London.
—— (1933). *Researches on Fungi Vol. V.* London.
BULMER, G. S. and BENEKE, E. S. 1964. Germination of basidiospores of *Lycoperdon* species and *Scleroderma lycoperdoides*. *Mycologia* **56**, 70–76.
ENGEL, H. and SCHNEIDER, J. C. 1963. Die Umwandlung von Glykogen in Zucker in den Fruchtkörpern von *Sphaerobolus stellatus* (Thode) Pers. vor ihrem Abschusz. *Ber. dt. bot. Ges.* **75**, 397–400.
GREGORY, P. H. 1949. The operation of the puff-ball mechanism of *Lycoperdon perlatum* by raindrops shown by ultra-high-speed Schlieren cinematography. *Trans. Br. mycol. Soc.* **32**, 11–15.
HEIM, R. 1948. Phylogeny and natural classification of macro-fungi. *Trans. Br. mycol. Soc.* **30**, 161–178.
ROMAGNESI, H. 1933. Le genre *Richoniella*, chaînon angiocarpe de la série des Rhodogoniosporés. *Bull. Soc. mycol. Fr.* **49**, 433–434.
SINGER, R. and SMITH, A. H. 1960. Studies on secotiaceous fungi XI. The astrogastraceous series. *Mem. Torrey bot. Club* **21**, 1–112.
SREERAMULU, T. and SESHAVATARAM, V. 1962. Spore content of air over paddy fields I. Changes in a field near Pentapadu from 21 September to 31 December 1957. *Indian Phytopath.* **15**, 61–74.
WALKER, L. B. and ANDERSEN, E. N. 1925. Relation of glycogen to spore-ejection. *Mycologia* **17**, 154–159.

VIII

SPORE LIBERATION IN
BRYOPHYTES

DISPERSAL in bryophytes is a large subject deserving of further study and particularly of experimental investigation. Here discussion is limited to spore release. The liberation of sperms by rain splash, or even by violent discharge as in *Conocephalum conicum* (Cavers, 1903), is not considered nor is the setting free of units of vegetative reproduction. Thus no account is given of the gemma-splash-cups of *Marchantia polymorpha*, although it is tempting to compare these in detail with the mature sporophores of bird's-nest fungi (Nidulariaceae). Further it is not proposed to discuss the actual dispersal of spores, but merely how they escaped from their capsules.

With very few exceptions the spores of bryophytes are wind dispersed and liberation occurs under dry conditions. However, the equipment concerned with this initial process is so different in liverworts and mosses that the two groups must be considered, in the main, separately.

Perhaps the commonest type of spore liberation in liverworts is that which occurs in most leafy genera (e.g. *Lophocolea, Cephalozia, Calypogeia, Diplophyllum*) and also in the thalloid genus *Riccardia*.

Cephalozia bicuspidata may be selected as a typical example from which most other leafy liverworts deviate only in small details. This species, common in Britain, has a prostrate stem with two rows of minute bifid leaves (Fig. 93). It fruits abundantly in the early spring. The sporogonium occupies a terminal position on a branch. At maturity the delicate fleshy stalk (seta) elongates very rapidly carrying the oval capsule upwards to a height of 1–2 cm. Elongation of the stalk, as in liverworts generally, involves enormous extension of individual cells without any cell-division.

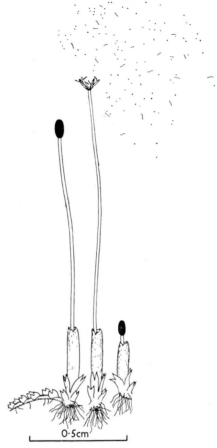

Fig. 93. *Cephalozia bicuspidata*. Left: plant with sporogonium emerging from the tubular perianth, the seta being fully elongated. Middle: similar plant with the capsule wall split into four teeth and with spores and elaters being flung out. Right: slightly younger sporogonium before major elongation of seta.

The structure of the ripe capsule is illustrated in Fig. 94. There is a hard two-layered wall. Within this, each stuck closely by one end to it, are the elaters which converge inwards and downwards towards the vertical axis of the capsule. The spores coat these elaters thickly. In the capsule-wall are four

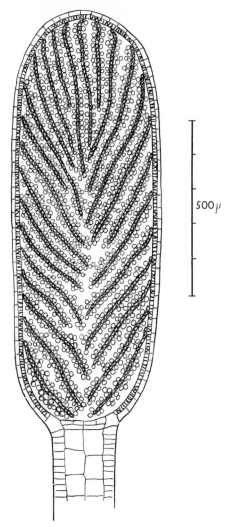

500 μ

FIG. 94. *Cephalozia bicuspidata*. Longitudinal section of mature capsule showing elaters, coated with spores, each attached by one end to the capsule wall.

lines of weakness radiating from the apex to the base of the capsule. Such is the nature of the thickening of the cells of the capsule wall that on drying strains are set up which are relieved by splitting along these dehiscence lines, thus carving out four small teeth which, as they diverge, expose the mass of spores and elaters.

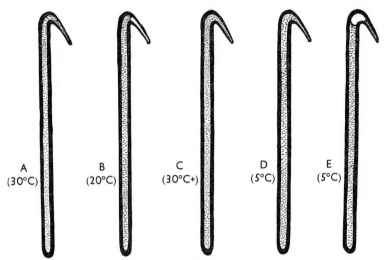

FIG. 95. *Berthelot's experiment.* A, thick-walled glass tube filled with water at 30°C, tip open; B, cooled to 20°C and then extreme tip sealed in flame; C, heated to over 30°C so that water again fills tube and air is forced into solution; D, now cooled to say 5°C when water continues to occupy whole tube; E, at same temperature but a few seconds later; water-rupture has occurred and the water has contracted to its normal volume at 5°C and a gas-phase has appeared.

Before considering what happens as drying proceeds, it will be necessary briefly to consider the physics of water in the tensile condition. For the present purposes this may best be illustrated by a consideration of Berthelot's experiment (Dixon, 1914). This is fairly easily performed and is very instructive in understanding spore discharge mechanisms involving the rupture of stretched water (Fig. 95).

A thick-walled glass tube, some 25 cm long and with an internal diameter of about 0·1 cm, is thoroughly washed to remove

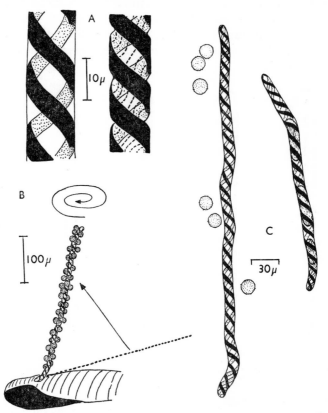

FIG. 96. *Cephalozia bicuspidata.* B, spore-coated elater attached to tooth of opened capsule: dotted line indicates its original position, and the straight arrow its early change in position; the other arrow represents the circular movement of the elater's free end as drying proceeds. A: left, portion of an elater before drying; right, as drying proceeds the thin-walled parts are sucked inwards and the elater is screwed up into a tighter spiral. C: right, a discharged elater just after mounting in water showing the presence of three gas bubbles; left, discharged elater after a minute or two of immersion now completely water-filled, some spores also shown.

all particles of dust and grease. It is then sealed at one end and drawn out at the other to form a fine crook that can dip into a small water reservoir. Then by alternate heating and cooling the tube can be completely filled with water at, say, 30°C. The tube is then removed from its reservoir and allowed to cool to 20°C, and in so doing the water in the tube contracts and draws in a very small volume of air. The open extreme tip is then sealed in a flame. If the tube is now heated to 30°C or rather more, the water again expands completely filling it, the air being forced into solution. If a bubble remains, even one only just visible with a strong lens, this simply enlarges if the tube is again cooled. However, provided the air has completely disappeared, on cooling the water continues to fill the whole tube even if the temperature falls below 10°C. The water is then in a state of tension. It is stretched, and this is possible because of the cohesion of the water molecules and of their adhesion to the glass walls of the tube. The tube itself, in spite of its thick walls, is no doubt also distorted to some extent. As cooling proceeds below 10°C, suddenly, and with an audible tinkle, the water ruptures and minute gas bubbles appear, which soon run together into one, the water contracting to its normal volume at the particular temperature involved (Fig. 95).

We may now return to the opening capsule of *Cephalozia* (Fig. 96) in which the spore-coated elaters, each loosely attached by one end to the capsule wall, are exposed to dry air. The elater is a longish tube (350–500 μ × 8–10 μ) with a thin cellulose wall, reinforced internally by two spiral bands of thickening, and filled with an aqueous solution. As water evaporates from it, the volume decreases. At first this decrease can be accommodated by the thin wall being sucked slightly inwards between twists of the spiral, but later this can be achieved only by the screwing of the thickening of the elater into a somewhat closer spiral. Actually as the elater dries its angle to the capsule wall first increases, and then the free-end performs an irregular rotary movement as the screwing-up process occurs. At this stage the water within the elater is in a state of tension. The now distorted spiral bands are tending to untwist, but this is prevented by the cohesion of the water molecules and by their adhesion to the cell-wall. The state of affairs is exactly like that in a Berthelot tube, except that it is evaporation, not cooling, that has led to the build-up of tension. As evaporation proceeds still further, a point is reached when the system breaks, a gas bubble appears and the elater returns instantaneously to its original form, untwisting with such violence that it breaks free from the capsule wall and springs into the air, throwing off its coating of spores in the process. The discharged and now undistorted elater has the form and appearance of an elater before any drying has occurred, but it is filled, in the main, with a gas phase, probably water vapour, and not with liquid. When observed dry under the microscope on a glass slide and subjected to rapid changes of humidity, such an elater shows no movement. If, however, a droplet of water is added to it, the gas phase quickly disappears and the elater again becomes full of liquid. Now when the topped-up elater is allowed to dry and watched under the microscope, it is seen to undergo writhing movements in the last stages of drying, and then suddenly shoots

Fig. 97. *Cephalozia bicuspidata.* Left: ripe capsule lying horizontally on a glass slide. Right: the same a few minutes later after the capsule has dehisced and discharge has occurred. The surrounding deposit consists of spores and elaters. ×16.

from the field of view as it springs violently from the slide at the moment of water-rupture. So an elater can be made to perform over and over again provided that, between each performance, it is again filled up with water.

Watched on a slide under the low power of a microscope the opening capsule of *Cephalozia*, or other leafy liverwort, looks like a miniature volcano in eruption as a shower of spores and elaters is discharged to a distance of several millimetres (Fig. 97).

Spore discharge mechanisms involving the rupture of stretched water seem to have evolved repeatedly in land plants and it may be legitimate to digress here from the general theme of spore liberation in bryophytes to give a comparative account of these mechanisms which are found in many ferns, some lycopods and certain fungi.

In most ferns the sporangial wall, consisting of a single layer of cells, has a line of specialized cells, the annulus, running from the stalk over the top and half way back to the stalk on the other side, where it joins the cells of the stomium (Fig. 98). Each annulus cell is heavily thickened on the innermost and on the radial walls but elsewhere the walls are thin. Each cell is at first filled with an aqueous solution. Evaporation leads to decrease in volume and the thin parts of the wall are sucked inwards to some extent. As a result of strains set up in the annulus, the sporangium splits in the region of the stomium and the slit enlarges sideways across the unspecialized cells of the sporangial wall so that the whole structure becomes separated into two little cups united only by the annulus. As each annulus cell loses further water not only is the thin part of the wall drawn inwards, but also the thick innermost part becomes bent to some extent, bringing the two thickened radial walls closer together. The effect of these changes is that the whole annulus bends slowly backwards carrying the upper cup containing most of the spores with it. In the annulus cells at this stage the water is under considerable tension, because each cell is tending to return to its original form and is prevented from doing so only by the cohesion of the water and its adhesion to the cell walls. Finally tension exceeds the critical

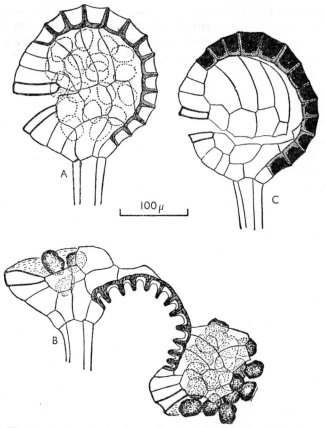

FIG. 98. *Dryopteris* sp. Behaviour of sporangium during drying. A, sporangium splitting at the stomium; annulus cells containing liquid. B, fully-open sporangium with annulus reflexed; each annulus cell is distorted and the volume of its aqueous contents is greatly reduced. C, sporangium in which the annulus has returned almost to its original position; annulus cells contain a gas phase shown black.

level and the water in an annulus cell breaks to give a gas phase. In a moment the cell returns to its former size and shape. The explosion in one cell appears to trigger off the others, with the result that the entire annulus almost instantaneously swings back to its original position slinging out the spores from the upper sporangial cup to a distance of a centimetre or so.

An essentially similar mechanism operates in connexion with the discharge of megaspores and microspores in *Selaginella*, except that two circular patches of specialized cells on either side of the sporangium, and not a linear annulus, are involved in the process.

In recent years it has been shown by Meredith (1961, 1962, 1963) that comparable water-rupture mechanisms are also a feature of certain fungi included in the dematiaceous Hypho-mycetes. The series of events associated with the discharge of the conidium in *Deightoniella torulosa* is illustrated in Fig. 99. The terminal cell of the conidiophore is thick-walled but the thickening is not deposited equally, being much less in the apical region. Resulting from this a change of form occurs on drying. As water evaporates from the cell the relatively thin-walled apex is drawn inwards. At this stage the watery contents are in a condition of growing tension as in a distorted liverwort elater or fern annulus cell. Eventually the water breaks, a gas phase makes its appearance, and in the same instant the cell returns to its original form discharging its conidium in so doing.

Another example is found in *Zygosporium oscheoides* (Fig. 99). In this the short conidiophore has a specialized, curved cell, referred to as a 'falx'. This has a dark, almost opaque, wall strongly thickened on the convex side, but relatively thin on the concave side. Apically this bears two small thin-walled cells each attenuated into a fine sterigma bearing a small oval spore. When exposed to dry air, evaporation leads to increased curvature of the 'falx', just as in the fern annulus cell which it rather resembles. When finally water-rupture occurs, the 'falx' returns immediately to its former shape jerking off the spores from their sterigmata in the process. Meredith has reported a number of other examples of this type of discharge which may well be widespread amongst dematiaceous Hyphomycetes (Meredith, 1963).

Returning to the consideration of liverworts it must be emphasized that although water-rupture mechanisms are involved in many species, in others violent spore discharge is brought about by the action of elaters without the breaking of stretched water being concerned. A notable example is

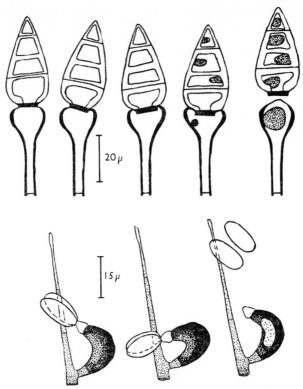

FIG. 99. Above: *Deightoniella torulosa*. Septate conidium attached to apical cell of conidiophore: stages in drying leading to spore discharge; gas-phase stippled. Only a minute fraction of a second separates the last two stages. Below: *Zygosporium oscheoides*. Changes on drying associated with spore discharge: the gas phase which finally appears in the 'falx' is shown white. Both after Meredith (1961, 1962).

Marchantia polymorpha (Fig. 100). In this the ripe capsule, at the end of a very short seta, hangs down from the underside of the archegoniophore, the positioning of the capsule appropriate to spore liberation being achieved by growth of the stalk of the archegoniophore and not, as in most liverworts, by elongation of the seta. Under dry conditions the wall of the capsule splits at the apex and rolls back exposing the spores and elaters which are rather long (about 500 μ). These as they dry begin to twist

176

and become entangled so that strains are set up relieved by jerking movements which throw the associated spores into the air. If an opening capsule is watched in bright sunlight a steady stream of spores, forming motes in the sunbeam, is seen

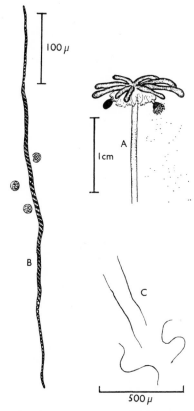

FIG. 100. *Marchantia polymorpha*. A, archegoniophore with two ripe capsules one of which is liberating its spores. B, an elater and three spores. C, above, two elaters under damp conditions, and below the same two in dry air.

descending from it. Finally the tangled elaters remain as a dry cottony mass from which most of the spores have escaped. Only rarely do the writhing movements result in the discharge of an elater, in striking contrast to *Cephalozia*. Although, the twisting which the elaters of *Marchantia* undergo on drying resembles exactly what happens at first in those of *Cephalozia*, no gas phase appears and there is no sudden and violent untwisting. In the drying elater of *Marchantia* the interior of the elater is reduced

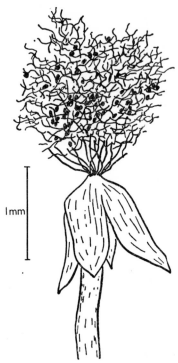

1mm

FIG. 101. *Pellia epiphylla*. Dehisced capsule after most of the spores have been blown away. There is a tuft of fixed elaters and a few residual spores are still trapped amongst the mass of free elaters.

to practically nothing without the strain on the water, produced by the tendency of the distorted spiral to untwist, becoming sufficiently great to cause water rupture.

It is interesting to note that this type of spore-liberating mechanism, involving the violent hygroscopic movements of spirally-thickened elaters, is also a feature of species belonging to the slime-mould genus, *Trichia*.

In *Pellia epiphylla* (Fig. 101), the liverwort 'type' for so many elementary students, the spiral thickening of both fixed and free elaters appears to be weak and only feeble hygroscopic movements occur even with sudden, drastic changes in the humidity of the air. Violent spore discharge does not seem to occur to an appreciable extent. This does not mean that spore liberation is inefficient. The seta is exceptionally tall, so that the capsule is often placed more favourably for spore take-off than it is in most liverworts. The dry spores are easily blown away, but only if air currents are sufficiently strong. A system in which the wind speed must exceed a certain value before spores are set free may well have a distinct value.

In *Anthoceros*, with a sporogonium quite unlike that of other liverworts, spore release also seems to be essentially non-violent. The author has watched spore release in a species collected in Jamaica (Fig. 102). The sporogonium, rather like a cylindrical blade of grass, opens progressively from the apex downwards and splits gradually into two valves exposing the central rod-like columella with which are associated spores and filamentous pseudo-elaters each often composed of several cells. The dry spores occur emeshed in a mass of these and are in due course blown away. Hygroscopic movements of the elaters seem to be too feeble to cause any active spore liberation.

The following account is given by Proskauer (1948) based on the British species *A. laevis*: 'In undisturbed capsules, growing under natural conditions, splitting along the dehiscence-lines generally appears to stop short of the actual apex. The valves, which progressively become detached downwards as ripening proceeds, become twisted spirally as they dry. This twisting is a reversible hygroscopic reaction, although the valves do not respond to slight changes in atmospheric humidity (e.g. those caused by breathing) such as will induce strong movements in other hygroscopic structures like the peristome teeth of mosses. In a very humid atmosphere, however, . . . the valves almost completely untwist and close the sporogonium'. He suggests that movement of the valves and pseudoelaters have little effect, but that spores are easily blown out of the opened capsule by air currents.

Violent spore discharge with the elaters actively concerned is

179

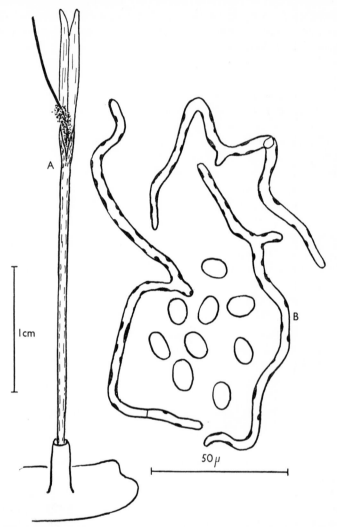

FIG. 102. *Anthoceros* sp. A, capsule opening by two valves exposing the columella with adhering pseudoelaters. B, spores and three pseudoelaters. Drawn from an unnamed species collected in Jamaica.

found in species of *Frullania*. However, although evaporation is responsible for operating the mechanism, neither hygroscopic movements of the elaters (as in *Marchantia*) nor water rupture in them (as in *Cephalozia*) is involved.

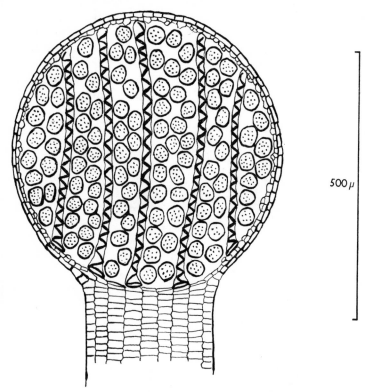

500 μ

FIG. 103. *Frullania dilatata*. Capsule in longitudinal section.

The description which follows is based on *F. dilatata*, a common species growing abundantly as brownish patches on the bark of trees in the damper parts of Britain. The spherical capsule, which ripens in late spring, is raised on a stalk only about half a centimetre long. Inside are many rather large spores and some 50–60 elaters (Fig. 103). One end of each of these is attached to the roof and the other to the base of the capsule. The unique behaviour of this capsule in relation to spore liberation was described towards the end of last century (Kamerling, 1898).

Dehiscence can usually be induced if a perfectly ripe capsule is placed in dry air. The splitting of the capsule wall and the discharge of spores occupies only a few seconds. Strains are set upon drying in the capsule wall which lead to dehiscence along four lines of weakness, as in most liverworts, and four little teeth of wall tissue bend rapidly backwards. Each tooth has, near its tip, about fifteen elaters firmly attached, with their other ends much less securely stuck to the base of the opening capsule. As

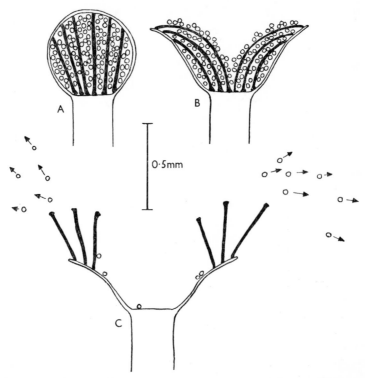

Fig. 104. *Frullania dilatata*. A–C stages in the process of spore discharge; elaters shown black. C is a fraction of a second after B; arrows indicate direction of movement of spores.

the teeth bend further outwards the elaters, each with a single spiral band of thickening, are stretched. At first the teeth diverge rapidly; then there is a pause with the elaters in a stretched condition. Suddenly and almost simultaneously they break free from their basal attachment and as they contract their free ends swing into the air. At the same time the segments of the capsule wall, no longer restrained by the stretched elaters, spring backwards to some extent. These violent movements are responsible for throwing the spores 1–2 cm into the air (Figs. 104 and 105).

After spore discharge the elaters undergo slight twisting movements as they dry, but these have no significance in discharge since they occur after the spores are scattered. As with the elaters of *Marchantia* no gas phase appears in their interior.

Thus in *Frullania* spore discharge depends largely on stretched spiral springs which, when they contract, fling the associated spores into the air.

Leaving liverworts for the time being we may pass to a consideration of spore liberation in mosses. In these there are no elaters in the capsule which, instead of dehiscing along four lines of weakness, usually opens by a lid.

In mosses there is a considerable range in spore liberating mechanisms. Perhaps the most divergent type is found in *Sphagnum* which in many respects differs so strongly from other mosses that some bryologists would isolate it in a subphylum of its own. The capsule is spherical, 2–3 mm in diameter, and when ripe is raised on a stalk 2–3 cm long. The dark brown, globose capsule on its fleshy stalk bears a striking superficial resemblance to the sporogonium of a liverwort, but structurally it is quite different and the stalk (pseudopodium) is actually part of the gametophyte.

A longitudinal section through a nearly ripe capsule shows (Fig. 106), within the epidermis, a mass of thin-walled parenchymatous tissue and a dome-shaped spore-sac containing the spores. By the time the capsule is ripe, much of the parenchyma has broken down leaving the spore-sac in the upper part, and below it a large space filled with air occupying most of the interior.

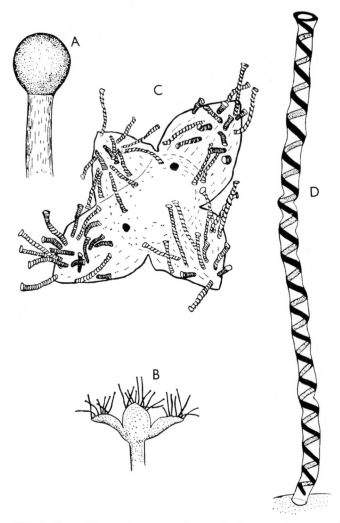

FIG. 105. *Frullania dilatata*. A, unopened capsule. B, opened capsule after discharge, three of the four 'teeth' of the capsule wall are visible. C, looking directly into a capsule after discharge; two residual spores are lying in its base. D, single elater with one end attached to 'tooth' of capsule wall. A and B × 24, C × 70, D × 290.

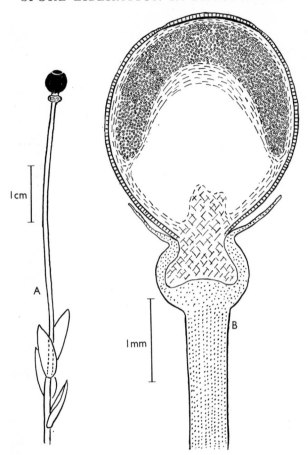

Fig. 106. *Sphagnum recurvum*. A, capsule raised on fleshy pseudopodium. B, longitudinal section of capsule; tissues indicated diagrammatically except for spores and capsule wall; note large air-space (shown white); remains of calyptra form collar around capsule base; the foot is immersed in the swollen apex of the pseudopodium.

The wall of the ripe capsule consists of a firm epidermis, the lid being delimited by a circular line of weakness along which dehiscence finally occurs. The thickening of the epidermal cells is such that on drying they contract transversely but not longitudinally, with the result that the diameter of the capsule is considerably reduced, whilst its length stays the same. The cells of the lid undergo little or no shrinkage as they dry and so the lid remains practically unaltered in size and form. Thus the capsule becomes somewhat cylindrical as evaporation proceeds (Fig. 107) and this leads to compression of the air within. Further, differences in behaviour of the cells of the lid and of the rest of the capsule-wall on drying result in stresses

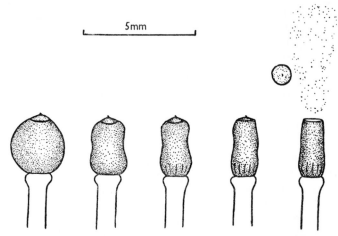

FIG. 107. *Sphagnum* stages in drying leading finally to spore discharge.

being set up along the line of junction. Finally these stresses lead to rupture. As soon as this happens the compressed air within the capsule expands explosively, bursting through the weak spore-sac, throwing off the lid, and blowing a cloud of dry powdery spores to a height of 15 cm or more. The sharp noise of the little explosion can be heard several yards away.

By trapping the air from a capsule dehiscing in absolute alcohol, and by comparing the volume of gas liberated with that of the capsule just before discharge, an estimate can be made of the pneumatic pressure at the moment of dehiscence. The average value has been found to be about five atmospheres (Nawaschin, 1897).

The whole process of spore discharge in *Sphagnum* is easy to observe if ripe capsules are brought into a room and placed within a few yards of a fire. In nature discharge probably occurs in dry sunny weather when turbulence is likely to be at a maximum.

In most mosses the dry mature capsule is at first closed by a lid, but when this falls off the mouth is usually still more or less guarded by an elaborate system of peristome teeth. The beauty and complexity of the peristome is a striking feature of many mosses and the behaviour of the teeth profoundly affects spore liberation. However, in a few mosses, e.g. *Pottia* spp., there is no peristome and the spores are directly and continuously exposed in an open but always erect capsule.

There is considerable range in peristome structure, but here only a few examples will be discussed. In the first place a rather elaborate type may be considered illustrated by reference to two common British mosses *Eurhynchium confertum* and *Mnium hornum*, both with closely similar peristomes (Ingold, 1959).

The peristome teeth are derived from a specialized layer of cells forming a hollow cone open at its extreme apex and with its circular base bedded on the rim (diaphragm) of the capsule (Figs. 108 and 109). As the capsule dries during its final stages of maturation most of the thin-walled parenchyma (dotted in Fig. 108) breaks down, the persistent tissues being the operculum, the epidermis (which forms the capsule wall), the diaphragm, the peristome, the columella (in a very shrunken state), and the spores. Except the spores, all these tissues finally consist of deal cells. The conical peristome layer, one-cell thick, separates, by rupture of the thin radial cell-walls, into an inner relatively thin sheet of wall material and an outer sheet locally very much thickened. By breakdown of regions of unthickened wall, both of the originally conical sheets become dissected from the apex downwards into teeth. In the outer peristome dissection extends to the junction with the diaphragm thus separating the teeth from one another, but in the inner splitting ceases considerably short of the base of the cone (Fig. 110). In transverse section of the maturing capsule towards its upper end the peristome is represented by a circle of sixteen cells (Fig. 111). Each outer peristome tooth is essentially a two-ply structure. In the section it is seen that the inner layer

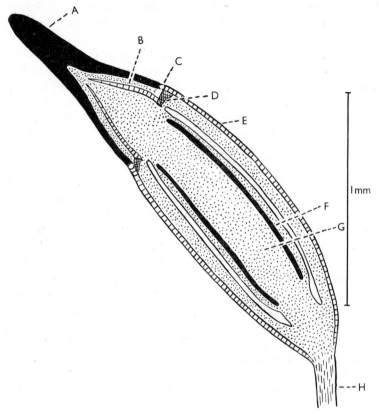

Fig. 108. *Eurhynchium confertum.* Longitudinal section through an immature capsule. A, operculum; B, peristome; C, annulus; D, diaphragm; E. capsule wall; F, spore sac; G, columella; H, seta. Thin-walled parenchymatous tissue is indicated by dotting.

of the tooth is the thickened outer wall of a peristome cell, and the outer layer the thickened inner walls of two cells immediately to the outside. Each tooth of the inner peristome is relatively thin and in section is seen to consist of the persistent inner tangential walls of two adjacent half cells. Thus the inner teeth alternate with the outer ones. At a level nearer the diaphragm the inner peristome is continuous and not dissected into teeth. There is a further complication. In the gap between

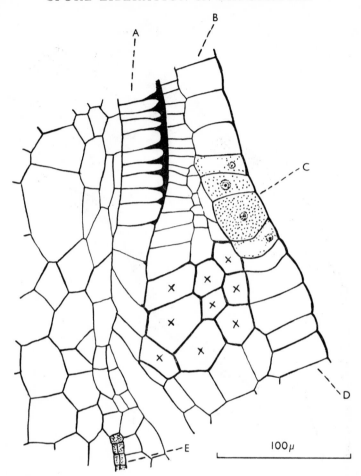

FIG. 109. *Eurhynchium confertum*. Details of part of section shown in Fig. 108. A, peristome B, operculum; C, cells of annulus; D, capsule wall; E, spore sac. Cells of the diaphragm marked 'x'.

each pair of inner teeth are two or three 'cilia'. These, like the teeth, are persistent parts of the inner sheet of cell-wall material constituting the inner peristome. The cilia are very flexible, but the inner teeth are stiff, each being V-shaped in section with the angle forming a spine facing outwards. In *Mnium* this

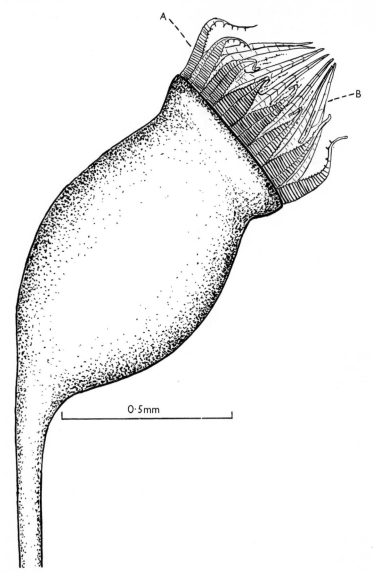

FIG. 110. *Eurhynchium confertum*. Mature capsule showing peristome. To simplify the picture the back half of the peristome is not shown. A, outer peristome. B, inner peristome.

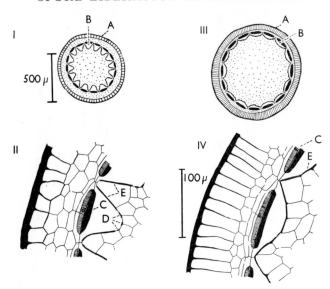

Fig. 111. *Mnium hornum*. I, transverse section of full-grown green capsule cut in operculum region half way between diaphragm and the tip. Cells of the operculum (A) and of the peristome (B) are shown, but the remaining thin-walled tissues are indicated by stippling. II, a small part of I giving high power details; C, outer peristome tooth; D, three cilia; E, inner peristome tooth. III, transverse section similar to I but nearer the diaphragm: A, cells of operculum, and B, cells of peristome. IV, high power details of part of III: C, outer peristome; E, inner peristome not dissected at this level.

angular spine is missing in the middle region of the tooth (Fig. 112).

In the peristome the outer teeth move in response to changes in humidity. This movement is due to the different behaviour of the two layers of each tooth. The outer is strongly hydrophilic, whilst the inner has little or no affinity for water. Thus in damp air the outer layer absorbs water and increases in length relative to the inner, so that the whole tooth curves inwards arching over a gap between two inner teeth and depressing the cilia in so doing. In *Eurhynchium* the inner layer of the tooth is optically fairly homogeneous. However, the

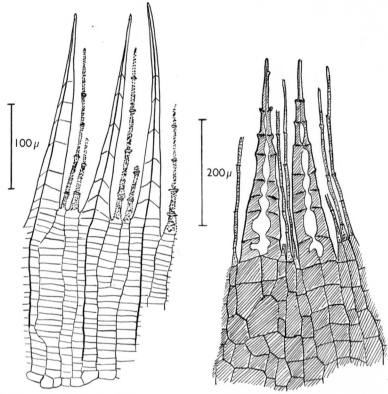

FIG. 112. A, *Eurhynchium confertum:* part of inner peristome (viewed from outside) showing three inner teeth and the cilia between. B, *Mnium hornum:* part of the inner peristome (looking at the inner surface) showing two teeth and a number of cilia.

outer layer consists of numerous transverse plates about 0·5 μ thick and much the same distance apart with the plane of each plate at right angles to the length of the tooth. Probably the space between the plates in a dry tooth is occupied by air. If this is so the actual surface for water absorption is enormous, and this may partly explain the rapid response of the tooth to an increase in humidity (Fig. 113).

In *Eurhynchium* spores may be shaken from the capsule under dry conditions, but they may also be violently discharged.

If a capsule of *Eurhynchium*, from which the lid has just separated, is laid on its side on a glass slide and examined with a hand lens, the process by which some of the spores are discharged can easily be observed. If the specimen is gently breathed upon, thus increasing humidity, the outer peristome

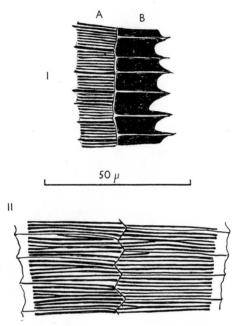

50 μ

FIG. 113. *Eurhynchium confertum.* Outer peristome. I, small part of a longitudinal section of a tooth: A, outer layer showing plates of thickening; B, inner homogeneous layer. II, view of outer surface of part of a tooth showing the plates of thickening.

teeth bend rapidly inwards, through the gaps between the inner teeth, depressing the flexible cilia as they do so. It would seem that in this state the capsule is more or less closed, and the tips of the incurved teeth become coated with spores from the upper regions of the full capsule. On drying the outer teeth swing rapidly backwards flinging out some spores to a distance of several millimetres. Further the serrate edges of the outer teeth

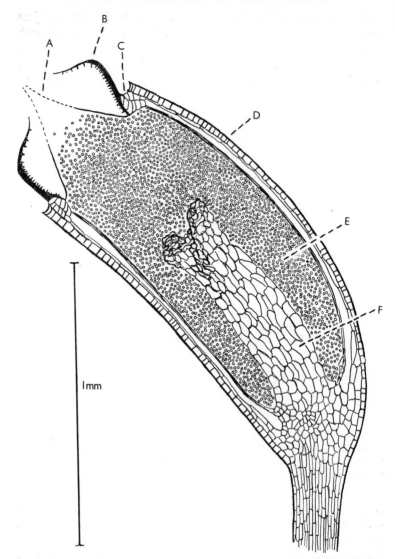

1mm

FIG. 114. *Eurhynchium confertum*. Longitudinal section of a mature capsule with the lid off. A, inner peristome; sectioned part shown by the continuous line, the general outline (not seen in the actual section) indicated by interrupted lines. B, outer peristome tooth. C, diaphragm. D, capsule wall. E, spores. F, columella.

may become momentarily caught on the erect teeth of the inner peristome and so move in a particularly jerky manner conducive to discharge. Also when an inner tooth, dragged backwards by a drying outer one, eventually snaps back to its original position, spores adhering to it may be violently discharged.

The number of spores in a capsule of *Eurhynchium confertum* varies from about a quarter to three-quarters of a million. In an experiment (Ingold, 1959) in which a recently opened capsule was breathed upon and then allowed to dry, and the process repeated 171 times, it was found that 15647 spores were violently discharged; an average of nearly a hundred at each backward movement of the outer teeth. Initially the numbers were much higher but fell steadily and, towards the end of the test, very few spores were being actively discharged. It is clear, therefore, that repeated drastic changes in humidity may lead to the discharge of many spores. However, since in *Eurhynchium confertum* the capsule faces upwards with its longitudinal axis at about 60° to the horizontal, movement of the outer peristome teeth cannot be responsible for the discharge of a large proportion of the spores. From a consideration of the mature capsule in sectional view (Fig. 114), it is difficult to see how more than 5–10 per cent of the spores could be scooped up by the teeth and thrown out. However, such a percentage would amount to many thousands of spores.

In *Mnium hornum*, where the capsule is nearly pendulous (Fig. 115), it is possible that movements of the peristome teeth might, perhaps, be more significant in discharge, since as spores, initially present within reach of the outer teeth, are liberated more may fall down and thus replenish the supply available to the activities of the teeth. In this connexion a vital point is whether the spores are dry or sticky. It has been stated that they are sticky, but this is not so. If a mature specimen with the lid still on is examined, the spore mass can be seen, through the translucent wall, half filling the capsule. If the capsule is inverted the spores drop down to the bottom behaving just like sand in an hour-glass. Thus as spores are liberated from the conical peristome region more may be expected to fall down and take their place. However, this does not mean that the peristome teeth are to a great extent concerned with active spore discharge. When conditions are dry and the outer teeth are reflexed, the powdery spores sift out through the inner peristome with the greatest of ease every time the wiry seta vibrates in a gentle breeze. Indeed, there is no reason to believe

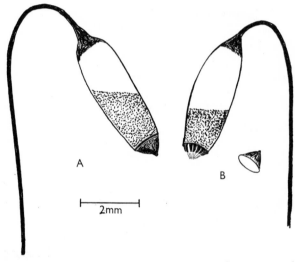

Fig. 115. *Mnium hornum.* A, ripe capsule—the operculum, seta, and extreme base of the capsule are opaque, but the spores (shown dotted) can be seen through the semi-transparent capsule wall. B, another capsule with the lid removed.

that in *Mnium*, any more than in *Eurhynchium*, violent discharge is of significant biological importance.

With such an elaborate structure as the moss peristome it is almost inconceivable that it is a mere decoration of use perhaps to the taxonomist but biologically negligible. However, it is only by careful experiment and observation in the field that its significance can really be evaluated. Most students of mosses would probably agree that fundamentally the importance of mobile peristome teeth is the closure of the capsule under damp conditions and the opening under dry. Violent discharge, when it occurs, may be regarded merely as an accidently concomitant of the opening mechanism.

Before giving further consideration to the possible value of spore liberation under dry conditions, it may be well to review certain other types of moss peristome.

For many elementary students the moss 'type' has been *Funaria hygrometrica*. However, in this the peristome is of a somewhat unusual form. As in *Mnium* and *Eurhynchium* there

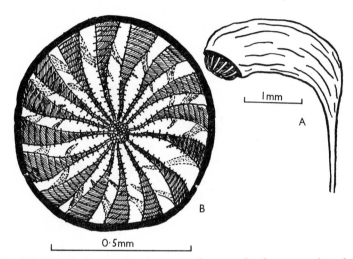

FIG. 116. *Funaria hygrometrica*. A, mature dry capsule after separation of the lid. B, looking directly into the mouth of the capsule under conditions of low humidity: the black circle is the diaphragm; the tips of the outer peristome teeth are united to a central disc. The free tips of inner teeth can be seen in the gaps between the outer teeth.

are two sets of teeth and it is only the outer which respond to changes in humidity. The inner teeth correspond in position with the outer and do not alternate. When looking directly into the capsule mouth, the outer teeth are seen to be curved and united by their tips to a small plate of dead cells (Fig. 116). Under damp conditions the teeth absorb water and elongate, but because they are fixed at both base and apex, this elongation simply has the effect of increasing their curvature. The whole outer peristome thus undergoes a twisting movement resulting in the almost complete closure of the slits between adjoining teeth, and so spore escape is prevented. The inner peristome appears to play little or no part in the mechanism.

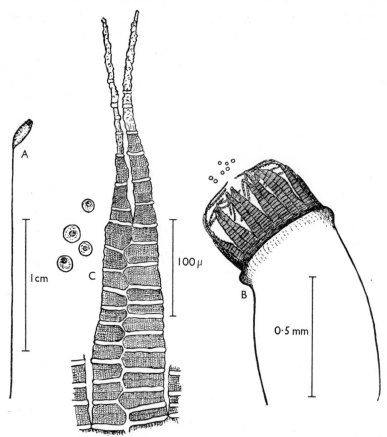

FIG. 117. *Dicranella heteromalla*. A, capsule on wiry seta. B, upper part of mature capsule showing single peristome (only front half shown). C, single outer tooth and four spores.

The inner teeth are not united by their apices and exhibit no hyposcopic movements. In *Funaria* there is no violent spore discharge.

In a number of mosses the inner peristome is lacking but the outer is well-developed, as in species of *Fissidens* and *Dicranella*. In the common moss *D. heteromalla*, which fruits so abundantly in early spring, each of the sixteen outer teeth is forked (Fig. 117). Under damp conditions these cover over the mouth of the capsule and the thread-like ends become entangled and coated with spores. On drying strains develop which are relieved by the ends of the teeth springing free, throwing spores into the air to a distance of a few millimetres. However, as in other mosses where violent discharge occurs by the action of the peristome, it seems that this is merely incidental to the opening process and is probably responsible for the liberation of only a small proportion of the spores.

In some mosses when the cap separates the mouth of the capsule is unguarded by teeth (e.g. *Pottia*) whilst in *Andreaea* there is no lid and the dry capsule opens by four longitudinal slits.

A peristome quite unlike that in other mosses is to be found in *Polytrichum* and *Atrichum*. In these genera thirty-two short teeth are fixed by their bases to the diaphragm their tips being attached to a relatively large epiphragm which stretches across the top of the capsule like the membrane of a drum. The teeth form a single ring and each is composed of a group of curved fibres. Its structure is, therefore, completely different from the peristome tooth of other mosses. Between the teeth are slit-like gaps. The whole mature dry capsule is very like a miniature poppy capsule (Fig. 118). The teeth show no hygroscopic movements, although it is possible that the size of the slits between them may be affected by the tautness of the 'drum' membrane, itself perhaps determined by the humidity of the air. Spores sift out between these slits. In some preliminary wind-tunnel experiments it has been found that at ordinary wind speeds practically no spores are liberated if the capsule is fixed so that its seta is not free to vibrate. When such freedom is allowed spores are readily shed. This emphasizes the importance of the dry wiry stalk in connexion with spore liberation in all mosses. It seems to be of considerable significance in release mechanisms generally and is in striking contrast to the fleshy seta of liverworts in which, since spore liberation depends essentially on the activity of elaters, the stalk is not directly concerned in the scattering mechanism, but only with placing the capsule in a suitable position for spore release.

If it is correct to assume that the major feature in the

survival value of the peristome to mosses is that spores are set free only under relatively dry conditions, there is the further question: What is the advantage of spores escaping when the air is dry? The answer is probably to be sought amongst other

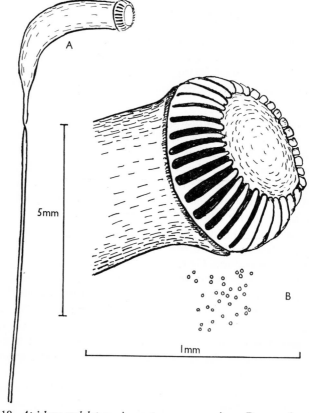

FIG. 118. *Atrichum undulatum*. A, mature sporogonium. B, apex in greater detail; the peristone teeth shown white and the spaces between them black. The tips of the teeth are bent inwards and attached to a drum-like membrane (epiphragm); some spores are also shown.

meteorological conditions closely correlated with dryness. As has been emphasized in connexion with fungi, for effective dispersal the spores must get into the region of eddies above the layer in immediate contact with the ground where the air is still or where its flow is merely laminar. The thickness of the non-turbulent layer varies with weather conditions. It may be only a few millimetres or, even at times a few microns, deep but when conditions become very still, as just after sunset, the laminar layer may be reckoned in metres. However, under such conditions the humidity close to the ground, which is usually damp, will tend to increase. There is probably a close correlation very near the ground between humidity and air movement. Thus in general the peristome teeth, in responding to humidity, allow the spores to be liberated when conditions are sufficiently turbulent to give a good chance of adequate dispersal.

In passing it might be remarked that, from the point of view of dispersal, the longer the seta the better. However, its possible height is probably limited by the absence of a vascular system. In other archegoniate plants, where such a system exists, spore liberating mechanisms are exposed much higher above ground level as in the fertile frond of *Blechnum spicant*, the spike of *Ophioglossum vulgatum*, the strobilus of *Lycopodium clavatum*, or the cone of *Equisetum arvense*.

The whole problem of spore liberation and aerial dispersal of bryophytes needs experimental study both in the laboratory and in the field. A preliminary study by Pettersson (1940) has contributed little beyond indicating some of the lines of work which might be followed.

It has been pointed out that in bryophytes dispersal is normally through the air and take-off mechanisms are clearly related to this type of dispersal. However, both in the liverwort genus *Riccia* (Fig. 119, A) and in such moss genera as *Pleuridium* (Fig. 119, B), *Phascum*, and *Ephemerum* there is no definite dehiscence mechanism. Associated with this the seta is either absent, as in *Riccia*, or very short, as in the cleistocarpic mosses, and also the spores tend to be exceptionally large. Spores are set free by the breakdown of the capsule walls in the mosses, and by decay of the thallus in which the spores are embedded in *Riccia*, and thereafter they may, perhaps, be dispersed by rainsplash or by animals. As often in the fungi so in bryophytes

increase of spore size seems to be associated with the abandon-
ment of normal aerial dispersal.

In bryophytes an isolated example of insect dispersal is
found in the remarkable moss *Splachnum*. In this the ripe

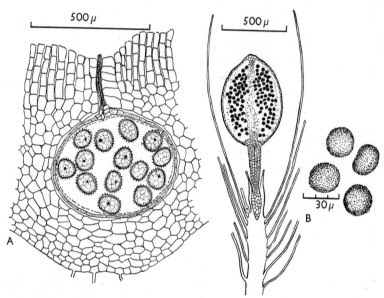

FIG. 119. A, *Riccia rhodesiae*. Vertical section of thallus. The capsule (with
its disorganized wall shown by a dashed line) is contained within the
calyptra. B, *Pleuridium subulatum*, vertical section of a mature sporogonium
attached to its gametophyte. Note the absence of any structural provision
in relation to dehiscence and the large spores.

sporogonium remains fleshy, the apophysis being relatively
enormous and brightly coloured (Fig. 120). After the lid falls
off the eight peristome teeth bend outwards exposing a mass of
spores which, instead of being powdery, are sticky and cannot
be dislodged by shaking. Species of *Splachnum* grow on old dung
of herbivores, and the spores appear to be distributed by
coprophilous flies. In the extraordinary species *S. luteum* the seta
may be up to 15 cm long and the small capsule is exposed in
the centre of a brightly coloured apophysis forming a disc which

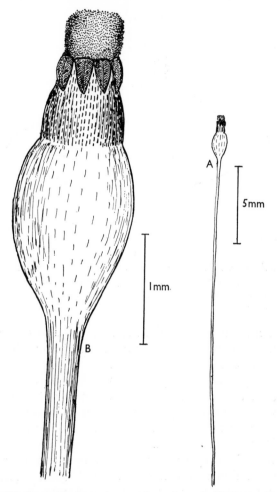

FIG. 120. *Splachnum sphericum*. A, capsule and top half of seta. B, capsule: a sticky mass of spores is seen above the ring of reflexed peristome teeth; there is a clear distinction between the upper, darker, spore-bearing region and the lower swollen apophysis.

203

Fig. 121. *Splachnum luteum*. Mature capsule; the columella protrudes through the sticky mass of spores, the peristome teeth are reflexed, the apophysis forms a collar around the spore-bearing region of the capsule. After Hedwig *et al*.

may be 2 cm in diameter (Fig. 121). As with *Aseroë* amongst the Gasteromycetes, this moss has produced something biologically much like an entomophilous flower.

Reviewing the whole question of spore liberation in bryophytes, it is clear that there is a considerable body of information about the morphology of capsules in relation to the release of spores and a reasonable understanding of how the various mechanisms work. What is conspicuously lacking is exact information about spore release under field conditions particularly in relation to the micro-meteorology at capsule level. However, with the refinement of techniques for spore-trapping and for measuring wind, temperature, and relative humidity close to the ground bryologists may be encouraged to turn their attention to this problem.

REFERENCES

CAVERS, F. (1903). Explosive discharge of antherozoids in *Fegatella conica*. *Ann. Bot.* **17,** 270–274.

DIXON, H. H. (1914). *Transpiration and the ascent of sap in plants.* London.

INGOLD, C. T. (1959). Peristome teeth and spore discharge in mosses. *Trans. bot. Soc. Edinb.* **38,** 76–88.

KAMERLING, Z. (1898). Der Bewegungsmechanismus der Lebermooselateren. *Flora* **85,** 157–169.

MEREDITH, D. S. (1961). Spore discharge in *Deightoniella torulosa* (Syd.) Ellis. *Ann. Bot.* **25,** 271–278.

—— (1962). Spore discharge in *Cordana musae* (Zimm.) Höhnel and *Zygosporium oscheoides* Mont. *Ann. Bot.* **26,** 233–241.

—— (1963). Violent spore release in some Fungi Imperfecti. *Ann. Bot.* **27,** 39–47.

NAWASCHIN, S. (1897). Ueber der Sporenausschleuderung bei der Torfmoosen. *Flora* **83,** 151–159.

PETTERSSON, B. (1940). Experimentelle Untersuchungen über die euanemachore Verbreitung der Sporenpflanzen. *Acta bot. Fenn.* **25,** 1–103.

PROSKAUER. J. (1948). Studies on the morphology of *Anthoceros* II. *Ann. Bot.* **12,** 425–439.

INDEX

207